Measurement of
Pyramids, Cyl
and Cones

Developed and Published
by
AIMS Education Foundation

This book contains materials developed by the AIMS Education Foundation. **AIMS** (**A**ctivities **I**ntegrating **M**athematics and **S**cience) began in 1981 with a grant from the National Science Foundation. The non-profit AIMS Education Foundation publishes hands-on instructional materials that build conceptual understanding. The foundation also sponsors a national program of professional development through which educators may gain expertise in teaching math and science.

AIMS Education Foundation
P.O. Box 8120, Fresno, CA 93747-8120 • 888.733.2467 • aimsedu.org

ISBN 978-1-60519-030-3

Printed in the United States of America

Welcome to the AIMS Essential Math Series!

Essential Math uses real-world investigations, comics, and animation to engage students and help them discover and make sense of key mathematical concepts.

The units in this series are narrowly focused, conceptually developed, and carefully sequenced to provide a continuum of introduction, development, and reinforcement of the essential ideas.

A typical *Essential Math* unit includes five components:

Investigations form the heart of each lesson. Through guided hands-on exploration, students discover and make sense of the essential ideas.

Comics provide a model of effective instruction and make the content knowledge explicit. Students can use them to review learning or clarify experiences from the investigations. They also provide reading within the content area.

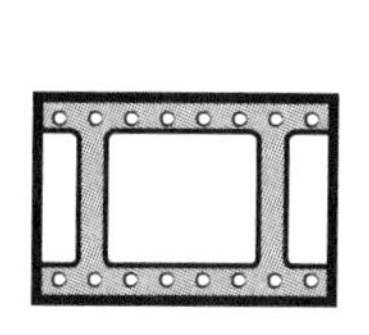

Animation and Video dynamically and visually summarize the essential concepts. They facilitate a deeper understanding and provide a powerful and meaningful memory.

Problem Solving activities help students apply and reinforce the concepts in unique ways.

Assessments provide an opportunity for students to apply their learning and for teachers to determine what depth of understanding has been gained.

The accompanying CD includes the comics and animations, as well as the student pages in pdf to facilitate printing and use on interactive boards. It may also include video help for activities as appropriate.

The comics and animations are also on our website (www.aimsedu.org) in case you want students to preview or review them as homework. The book contains a reduced-page version of the comics. The CD has both full-page and reduced-page versions so you can use the ones that best suit your needs.

Whether you use this unit in your regular classroom, for intervention, or as the basis for a summer school or after-school program, it will provide a rich and meaningful learning experience for your students.

Measurement of Prisms, Pyramids, Cylinders, and Cones

Table of Contents

Welcome to the AIMS Essential Math Series!

BIG IDEA: **All solids (boxes) can be folded from a flat form called a net. This net forms the surface of the box and its measure is called surface area.**

Lesson One: A Solid Review

Day 1

Lesson Two: Box Building

Day 2

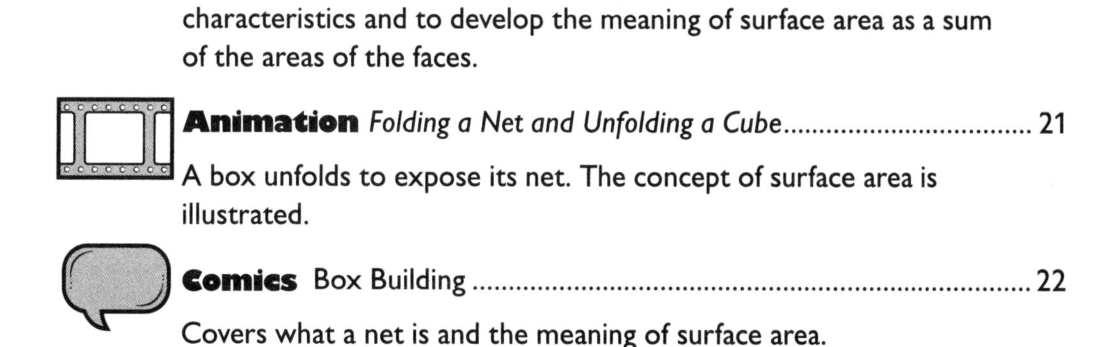

BIG IDEA: **The space inside a solid is its volume. By finding the area of a layer that covers the base (B) and multiplying by the number of layers *(h)*, one determines what it takes to fill the solid.**

Lesson Three: Filling Boxes

Day 3

Investigation *Filling Boxes* 25

By filling a box with cubes a layer at a time, students recognize the volume as a measure of filling and the relationship of volume to cubes in a layer and number of layers.

Animation *Boxes, Bases, and Blocks* 27

Seeing a rectangular solid built by row and layer provides a visual memory of the meaning and formula for finding the volume of a rectangular solid.

Day 4

Comics *Filling Boxes* 28

Emphasizes that volume is a measure filling and is reported in cubic units. It also helps students understand the formula for finding the volume of a rectangular-based prism.

Practice: Box Building and Filling 30

Provides an opportunity for students to apply their understanding of calculating surface area and volume to larger nets and solids.

Lesson Four: Special Box Building

Day 5

Investigation *Special Box Building* 33

Students use nets to build a triangular-based prism and a cylinder in order to understand their characteristics and to develop the meaning of surface area as a sum of the areas of the surfaces.

Animation *Unfolding Prisms and Cylinders* 36

A prism and cylinder unfold to expose their nets. The concept of surface area is illustrated.

Comics *Special Box Building* 37

Reviews formulas for finding the area of a triangle and circle, then progresses to summing the areas of all component parts to determine surface area.

Lesson Five: *Filling Special Boxes*

BIG IDEA: **The volume of a pyramid or a cone is one-third the volume of a prism or cylinder with the same base (B) and equal height.**

Lesson Six: *Building Pointed Boxes*

Lesson Seven: Filling Pointed Boxes

How can you use the similarities and differences of the geometric solids to identify each type?

Comparing and contrasting the different solids requires repeated examination, thereby providing a review of the names of the solids and a more extensive definition of each one. To measure surface area and volume of the solids, students will need to know the numbers and shapes of faces/surfaces along with how the solids are formed from nets.

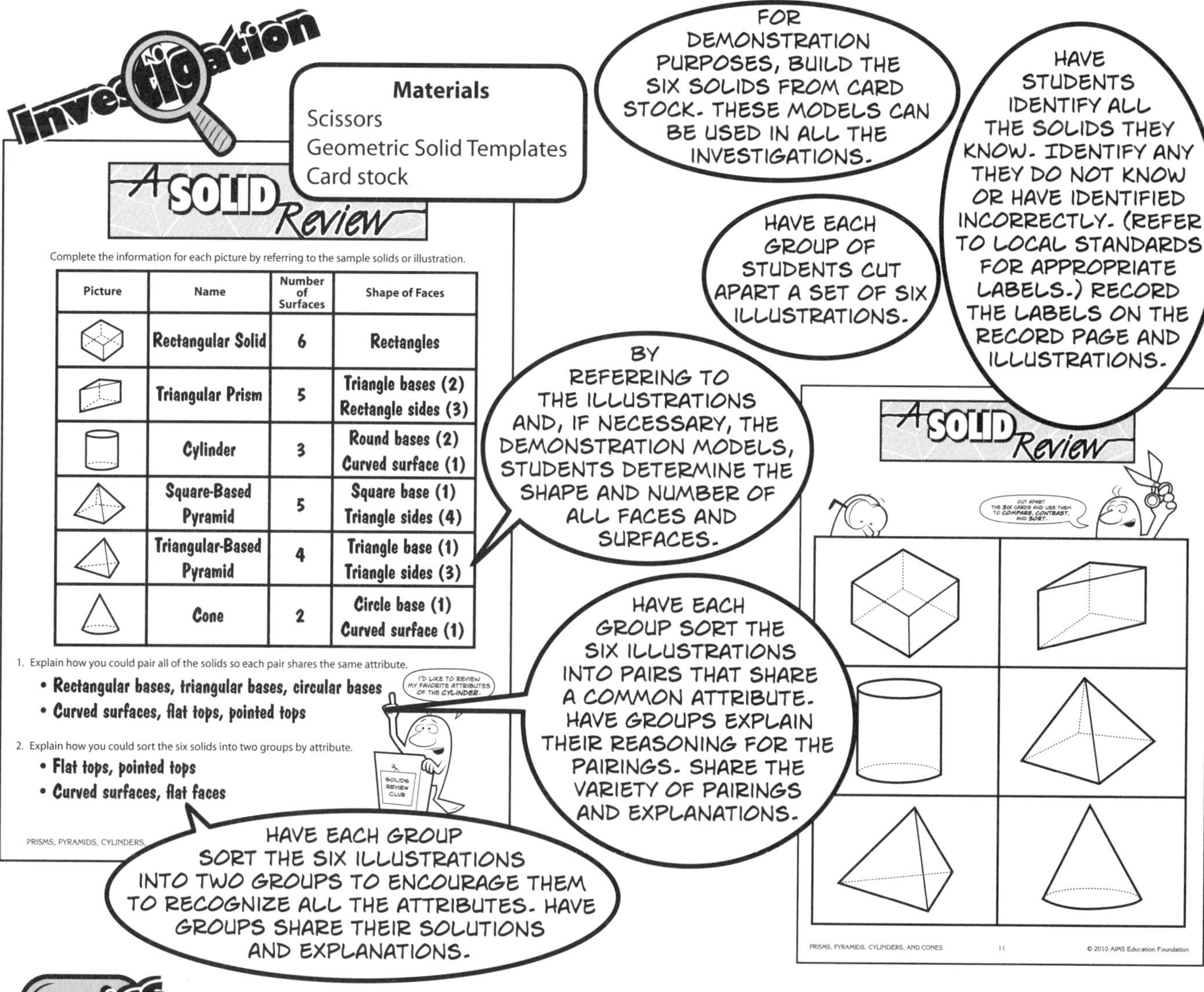

A SOLID Review

Complete the information for each picture by referring to the sample solids or illustration.

Picture	Name	Number of Surfaces	Shape of Faces
	Rectangular Solid	6	Rectangles
	Triangular Prism	5	Triangle bases (2) Rectangle sides (3)
	Cylinder	3	Round bases (2) Curved surface (1)
	Square-Based Pyramid	5	Square base (1) Triangle sides (4)
	Triangular-Based Pyramid	4	Triangle base (1) Triangle sides (3)
	Cone	2	Circle base (1) Curved surface (1)

1. Explain how you could pair all of the solids so each pair shares the same attribute.
   - Rectangular bases, triangular bases, circular bases
   - Curved surfaces, flat tops, pointed tops
2. Explain how you could sort the six solids into two groups by attribute.
   - Flat tops, pointed tops
   - Curved surfaces, flat faces

Reviews the attributes of six solids and helps clarify associated vocabulary.

Provides background of the general concepts related to solids including classifying, naming, and types of surfaces.

Complete the information for each picture by referring to the sample solids or illustrations.

Picture	Name	Number of Surfaces	Shape of Faces
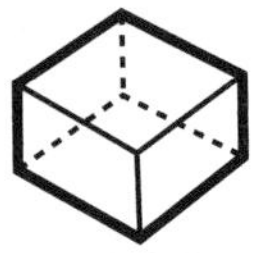			
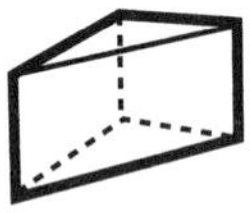			

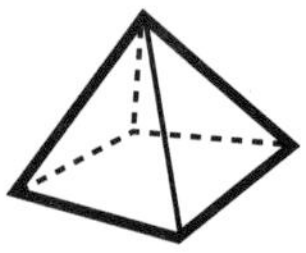			
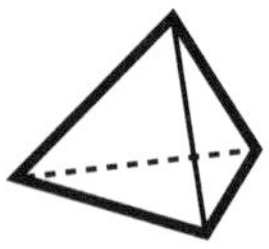			

1. Pair all of the solids so each pair shares an attribute. Explain your pairings.

2. Sort the six solids into two groups by attributes. Explain your sorts.

A SOLID Review
CUT APART THE SIX CARDS AND USE THEM TO COMPARE, CONTRAST, AND SORT.

Geometric Solid Template

What solid will this net make?

1. Cut out along the bold lines.
2. Fold along the dotted lines. (Use the edge of a ruler or the straight edge of a desk to get a sharp crease.)
3. Fold up into a solid using the tabs to tape or glue it.
4. Attach the top by gluing or taping the tab.

Enlarge to 103% when copying.

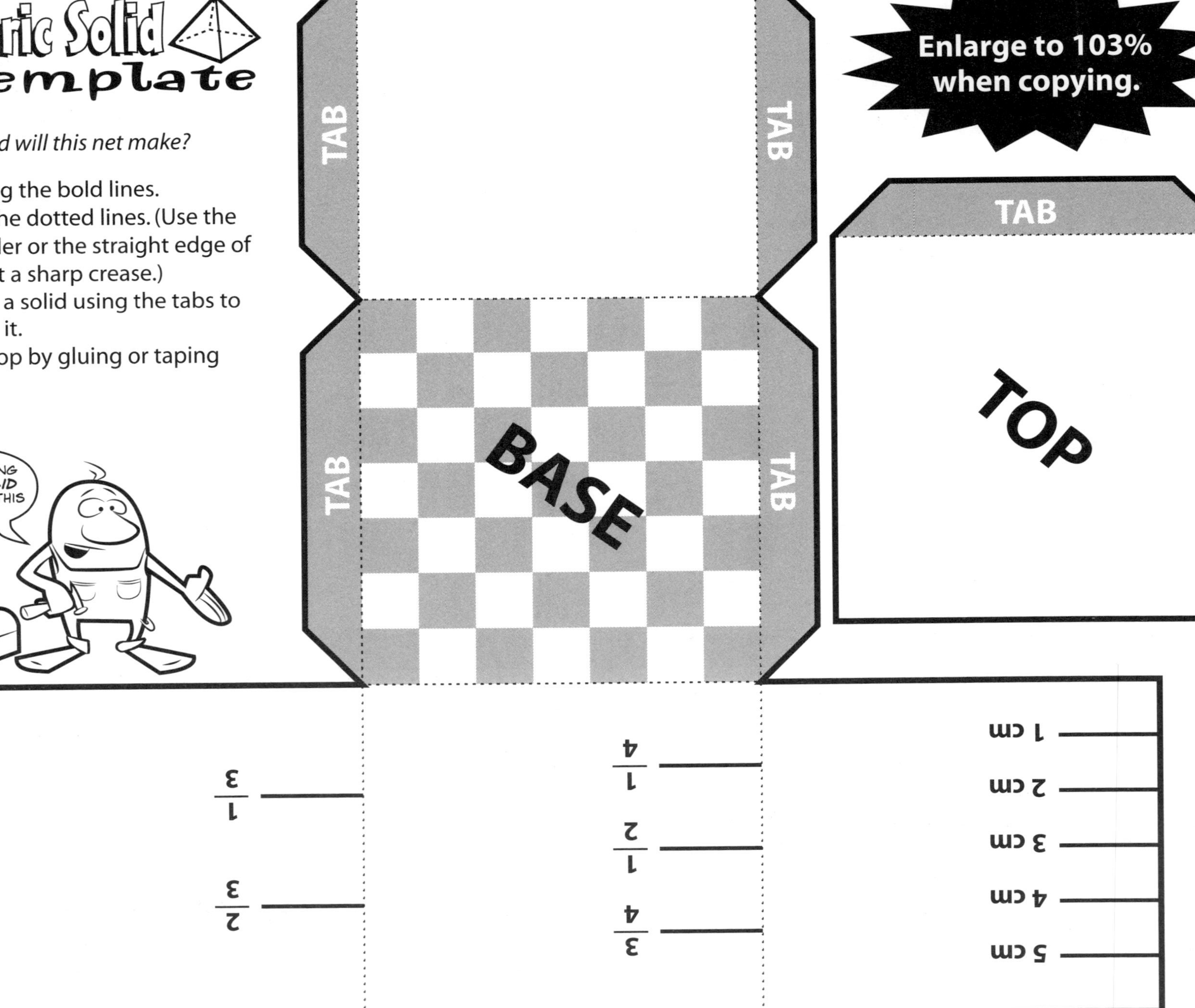

Geometric Solid Template

What solid will this net make?

1. Cut out along the bold lines.
2. Fold along the dotted lines. (Use the edge of a ruler or the straight edge of a desk to get a sharp crease.)
3. Fold up into a solid using the tabs to tape or glue it.
4. Attach the top by gluing or taping the tab.

TAB

$\frac{2}{3}$

$\frac{1}{3}$

$\frac{3}{4}$

$\frac{1}{2}$

$\frac{1}{4}$

5 cm

4 cm

3 cm

2 cm

1 cm

(This piece is used in *Filling Special Boxes.*)

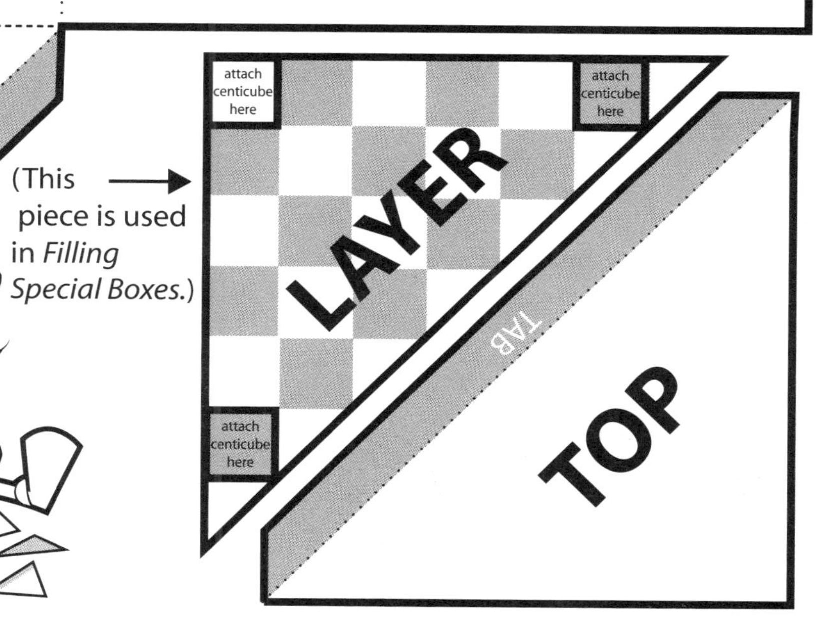

I HAVE AN *IDEA*!

YOU CONSTRUCT THE SOLID AND I'LL TAKE A *LUNCH BREAK*.

Geometric Solid Template

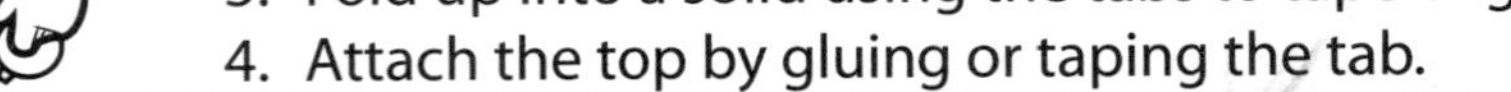

What solid will this net make?

1. Cut out along the bold lines.
2. Fold along the dotted lines. (Use the edge of a ruler or the straight edge of a desk to get a sharp crease.)
3. Fold up into a solid using the tabs to tape or glue it.
4. Attach the top by gluing or taping the tab.

DOES ANYONE HAVE A PHILLIPS **SCREWDRIVER?**

TAB
Match Line. Do not fold.

______ 5 cm

______ 4 cm

______ 3 cm

______ 2 cm

______ 1 cm

______ $\frac{3}{4}$

______ $\frac{1}{2}$

______ $\frac{1}{4}$

______ $\frac{2}{3}$

______ $\frac{1}{3}$

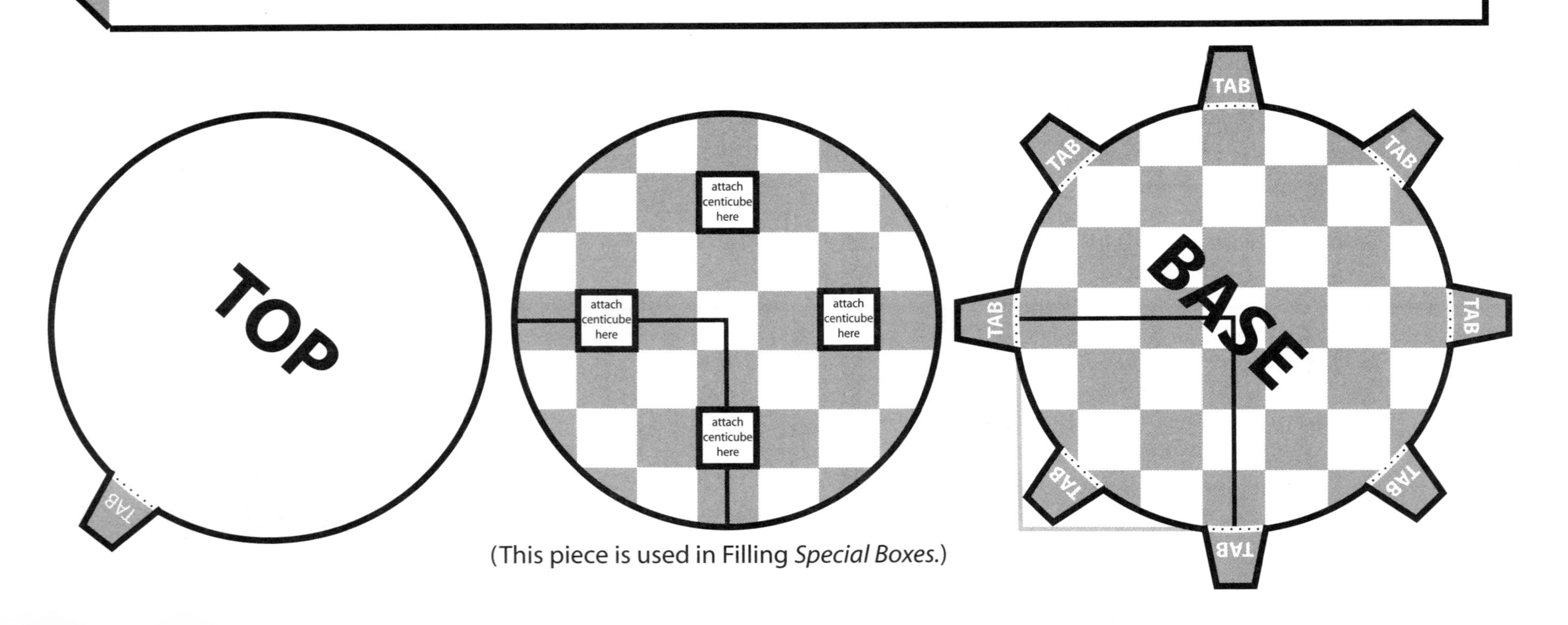

(This piece is used in Filling *Special Boxes*.)

Geometric Solid Template

What solid will this net make?

1. Cut out along the bold lines.
2. Fold along the dotted lines. (Use the edge of a ruler or the straight edge of a desk to get a sharp crease.)
3. Fold up into a solid using the tabs to tape or glue it.

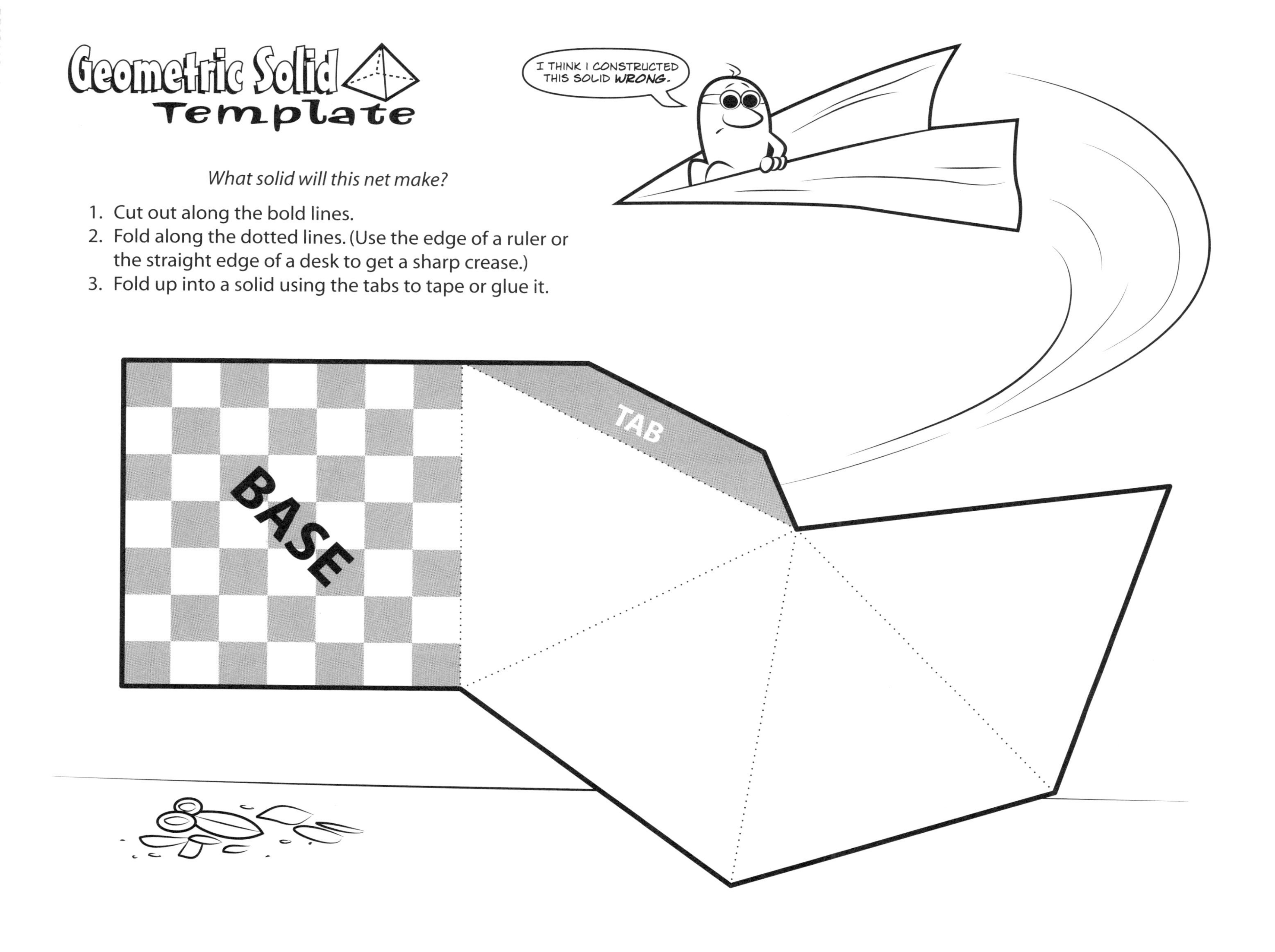

Geometric Solid Template

What solid will this net make?

1. Cut out along the bold lines.
2. Fold along the dotted lines. (Use the edge of a ruler or the straight edge of a desk to get a sharp crease.)
3. Fold up into a solid using the tabs to tape or glue it.

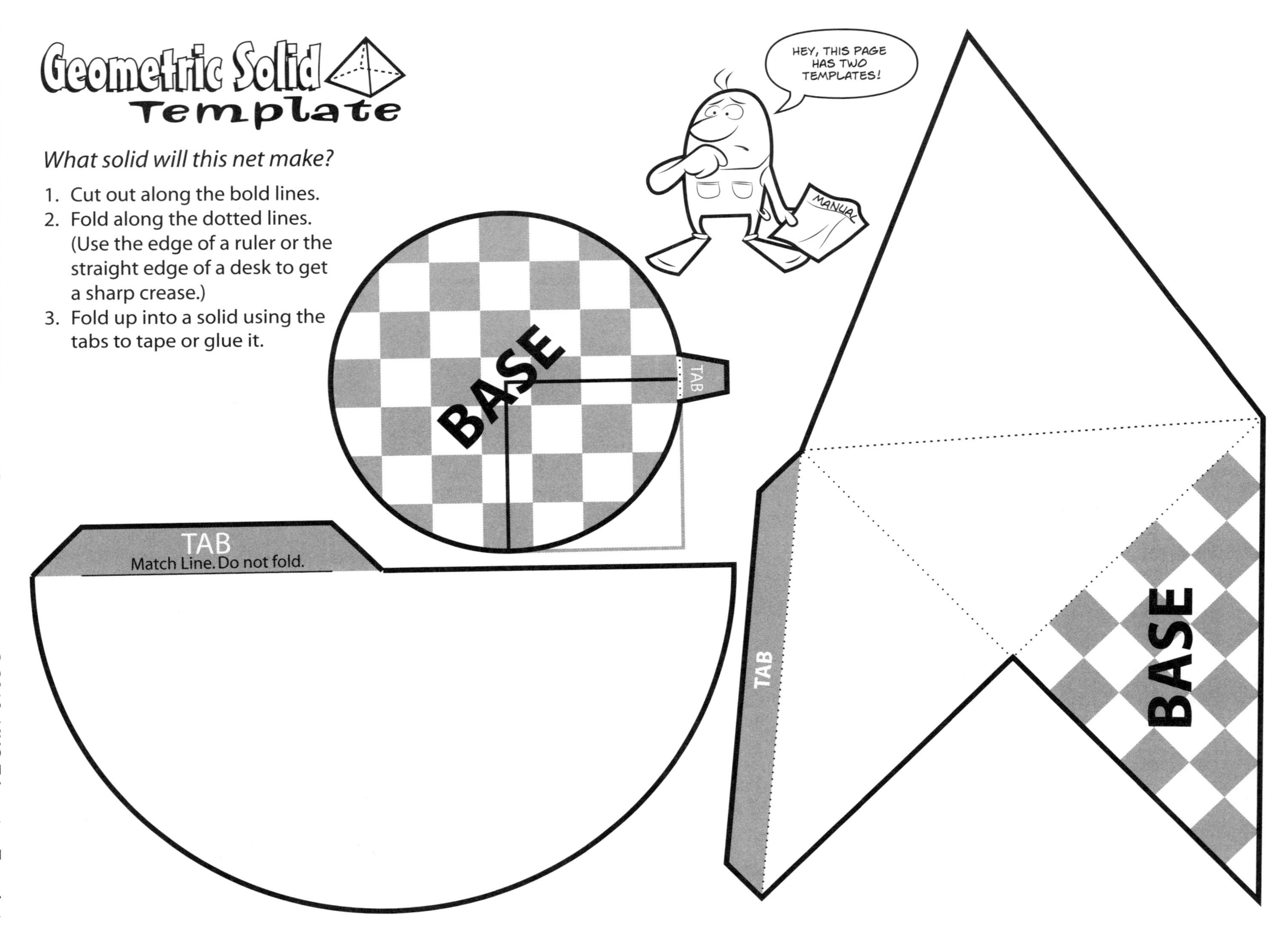

MEASUREMENT OF PRISMS, PYRAMIDS, CYLINDERS, AND CONES
ESSENTIAL MATH SERIES
A Solid Review
THINGS TO LOOK FOR:
1. WHAT DOES THE WORD SOLID MEAN IN GEOMETRY?
2. WHAT IS THE SHAPE OF A LATERAL FACE OF A PRISM?
3. WHAT IS THE SHAPE OF A LATERAL FACE OF A PYRAMID?
4. HOW IS A CYLINDER SIMILAR TO A PRISM?
5. HOW IS A CONE SIMILAR TO A PYRAMID?
CLASS, YESTERDAY WE REVIEWED THE NAMES OF SIX DIFFERENT SOLIDS AND WE TRIED TO DESCRIBE EACH OF THEM.
REMEMBER THAT IN MATH SOLID SIMPLY MEANS 3-DIMENSIONAL. PRISMS, CYLINDERS, CONES, AND PYRAMIDS ARE ALL 3-DIMENSIONAL SHAPES. SOMETIMES WE CALL THEM GEOMETRIC SOLIDS.
IN OUR ACTIVITY, WE LOOKED TO SEE WHICH ONES HAVE ONLY FLAT FACES AND WHICH ONES HAVE A CURVED SURFACE.
WE LOOKED AT THE NUMBER OF FACES AND THEIR SHAPES.
I KNOW YOU'RE QUITE FAMILIAR WITH THESE 3-DIMENSIONAL SHAPES FROM EARLIER GRADES, BUT THERE WERE A FEW WORDS THAT WERE NEW TO YOU, RIGHT?
FOR EXAMPLE, WHAT DO WE CALL THIS 3-DIMENSIONAL SHAPE?
IT'S CALLED A PRISM. IT'S THE SAME SHAPE AS THE GLASS PRISMS WE USED IN SCIENCE CLASS.
WE USED PRISMS IN SCIENCE CLASS? REALLY?
YEAH, REMEMBER YOU CAN SHINE A LIGHT ON A PRISM AND SEE COLORS LIKE A RAINBOW.
LET'S LOOK AT SEVERAL DIFFERENT PRISMS AND TALK ABOUT WHAT WE KNOW ABOUT THEM.
1
TWO OF THE FACES ARE ALWAYS CONGRUENT AND PARALLEL. THEY CAN BE SQUARES OR RECTANGLES OR TRIANGLES OR PENTAGONS OR ANY OTHER POLYGON SHAPE. THESE TWO OPPOSITE FACES ARE CALLED BASES OF THE PRISM.
THE SHAPE OF THE BASE OF A PRISM GIVES IT ITS NAME.
SO IF THE BASE IS A TRIANGLE, IT'S A TRIANGULAR PRISM, IF IT'S A SQUARE IT'S A SQUARE-BASED PRISM, AND SO ON.
ALL OF THE OTHER FACES OF A PRISM ARE RECTANGLES AND ARE CALLED LATERAL FACES.
LATERAL?? WHAT DOES THAT MEAN?
WELL, THE WORD LATERAL MEANS TO THE SIDE OR OFF TO THE SIDE.
LOOK AT THE PRISM THAT'S PICTURED HERE.
THE BASES ARE THE TRIANGLES AT THE TOP AND BOTTOM.
THE OTHER THREE FACES ARE RECTANGLES AROUND THE SIDES OF THE PRISM.
THOSE ARE THE LATERAL FACES.
DOES THAT MAKE SENSE, REDMOND?
YEAH, I THINK IT DOES.
I'VE HEARD OF THE WORD LATERAL.
I THINK THEY USE IT IN FOOTBALL.
YEP, THE QUARTERBACK IN FOOTBALL SOMETIMES THROWS THE BALL TO A RECEIVER WHO IS JUST TO HIS LEFT OR RIGHT SIDE INSTEAD OF DOWN FIELD.
THAT'S CALLED A LATERAL PASS.
I BET YOU DIDN'T KNOW THAT, MARK.
SURE, I KNEW THAT. I KNOW EVERYTHING.
2

THANK YOU, VANESSA. THAT'S EXACTLY RIGHT.
LATERAL FACES
CLASS, THESE TWO 3-DIMENSIONAL SHAPES ARE PYRAMIDS. HOW IS A PYRAMID DIFFERENT FROM A PRISM?
IT'S DIFFERENT BECAUSE THE PYRAMID JUST HAS ONE BASE. (SEE? EVERYTHING.)
IT'S ALSO KIND OF LIKE A PRISM, BECAUSE THE BASE OF A PYRAMID CAN BE A TRIANGLE, OR A SQUARE, OR SOME OTHER SHAPE LIKE THAT.
BUT THE OTHER FACES ON A PYRAMID ALL HAVE TO BE TRIANGLES, RIGHT?
THAT'S RIGHT, SHUTTLE.
ARE THOSE OTHER TRIANGLE FACES OF THE PYRAMID CALLED LATERAL FACES, TOO?
YES, THEY ARE. THAT'S A VERY GOOD QUESTION, ELORA.
SO, THE LATERAL FACES ARE AROUND THE SIDES NO MATTER WHAT THE 3-DIMENSIONAL SHAPE.
AND, IF IT'S A PYRAMID, THE LATERAL FACES ARE TRIANGLES AND IF IT'S A PRISM, THEY'RE RECTANGLES.
WOW, RED, NICE.
I GET IT. THE LATERAL FACES OF A PYRAMID ALL MEET AT ONE POINT, SO THEY HAVE TO BE TRIANGLES.
MS. CHO, I DIDN'T KNOW THAT THE TOP POINT ON A PYRAMID COULD BE OFF TO ONE SIDE LIKE THAT.
I THOUGHT THE POINT WAS ALWAYS KIND OF RIGHT OVER THE MIDDLE OF THE BASE?
YOU'RE RIGHT. MOST OF THE PYRAMIDS YOU'VE SEEN BEFORE THESE WERE LIKE THAT. BUT, IT'S OKAY FOR THE POINT TO BE OFF TO THE SIDE LIKE IT IS ON THAT ONE.
FINALLY, CLASS, LET'S TALK ABOUT THE CYLINDER AND THE CONE.
THINK ABOUT THE NUMBER OF BASES IN A PRISM AND IN A PYRAMID.
3
HOW ARE THE CYLINDERS AND THE CONE SIMILAR TO THE PRISM AND THE PYRAMID?
I KNOW!
THE CYLINDER HAS TWO BASES JUST LIKE THE PRISM AND THE CONE HAS ONLY ONE BASE JUST LIKE THE PYRAMID.
MS. CHO, IT LOOKS LIKE THE CYLINDER AND THE CONE EACH JUST HAVE ONE LATERAL FACE.
THE FACE IS JUST ONE PIECE AND IT CURVES AROUND THE BASE, RIGHT?
LET'S SEE IF I CAN ANSWER ELORA'S QUESTION. HOW ABOUT INSTEAD OF CALLING IT A LATERAL FACE, LET'S CALL IT A CURVED LATERAL SURFACE.
THAT MEANS THAT A CYLINDER HAS TWO BASES THAT ARE CIRCLES, AND ONE CURVED LATERAL SURFACE.
THE CONE IS JUST LIKE IT, EXCEPT IT HAS ONLY ONE CIRCULAR BASE.
ON THE CONE, THE CURVED LATERAL SURFACE COMES TO A POINT AT THE TOP.
THAT'S JUST LIKE HOW ON THE PYRAMID THE LATERAL FACES ALL COME TO A POINT AT THE TOP.
MS. CHO, ISN'T A CYLINDER REALLY JUST LIKE A PRISM THAT HAS BASES THAT ARE CIRCLES?
OR, YOU COULD SAY THAT A PRISM IS LIKE A CYLINDER THAT HAS BASES THAT ARE TRIANGLES OR SQUARES OR SOME OTHER SHAPE.
WHAT??? WHAT ARE YOU SAYING? ISN'T A CYLINDER A CYLINDER AND A PRISM A PRISM.
YOU'RE RIGHT, REDMOND, BUT THEY ARE A LOT ALIKE. THAT'S ALL SHUTTLE AND VANESSA HAVE BEEN TRYING TO SAY.
YEAH, I GUESS THEY ARE A LOT ALIKE. OH, AND SO ARE THE PYRAMID AND THE CONE, RIGHT?
THAT'S RIGHT, REDMOND.
CLASS, THIS IS A GOOD START. WE'RE GOING TO BE DOING A LOT MORE WITH THESE SHAPES.
4

Box Building

How do you determine how much cardboard it takes to build a box in the shape of a rectangular solid (prism)?

Building a box from a net is an opportunity to identify the shapes used to make all the surfaces of a solid. Seeing the net reinforces the idea of surface area as a measure of covering and a sum of all the areas of each surface surrounding the the solid.

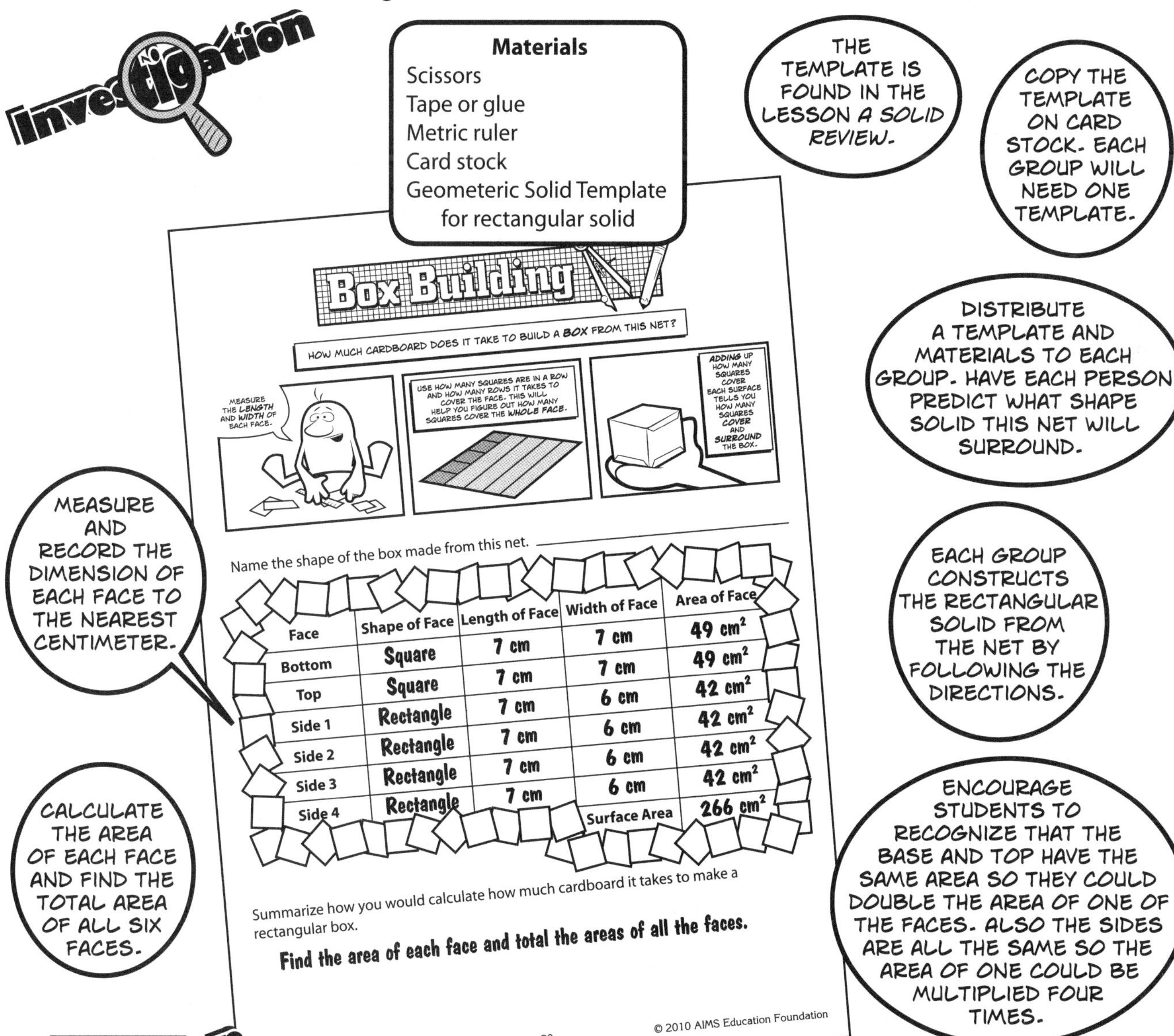

Box Building

HOW MUCH CARDBOARD DOES IT TAKE TO BUILD A BOX FROM THIS NET?

MEASURE THE LENGTH AND WIDTH OF EACH FACE.

USE HOW MANY SQUARES ARE IN A ROW AND HOW MANY ROWS IT TAKES TO COVER THE FACE. THIS WILL HELP YOU FIGURE OUT HOW MANY SQUARES COVER THE WHOLE FACE.

ADDING UP HOW MANY SQUARES COVER EACH SURFACE TELLS YOU HOW MANY SQUARES COVER AND SURROUND THE BOX.

Name the shape of the box made from this net.

Face	Shape of Face	Length of Face	Width of Face	Area of Face
Bottom	Square	7 cm	7 cm	49 cm²
Top	Square	7 cm	7 cm	49 cm²
Side 1	Rectangle	7 cm	6 cm	42 cm²
Side 2	Rectangle	7 cm	6 cm	42 cm²
Side 3	Rectangle	7 cm	6 cm	42 cm²
Side 4	Rectangle	7 cm	6 cm	42 cm²
			Surface Area	266 cm²

Summarize how you would calculate how much cardboard it takes to make a rectangular box.

Find the area of each face and total the areas of all the faces.

PRISMS, PYRAMIDS, CYLINDERS, AND CONES 20 © 2010 AIMS Education Foundation

Animation A box unfolds to remove its skin leaving its net and interior. The concept of surface area is illustrated.

Comics Covers what a net is and the meaning of surface area.

HOW MUCH CARDBOARD DOES IT TAKE TO BUILD A ***BOX*** FROM THIS NET?

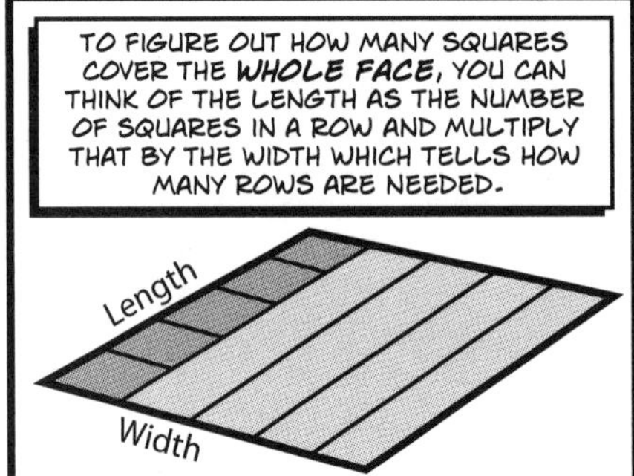

Name the shape of the box made from this net. ________________________

Face	Shape of Face	Length of Face	Width of Face	Area of Face
Bottom				
Top				
Side 1				
Side 2				
Side 3				
Side 4				
			Surface Area	

Summarize how you would calculate how much cardboard it takes to make a rectangular box.

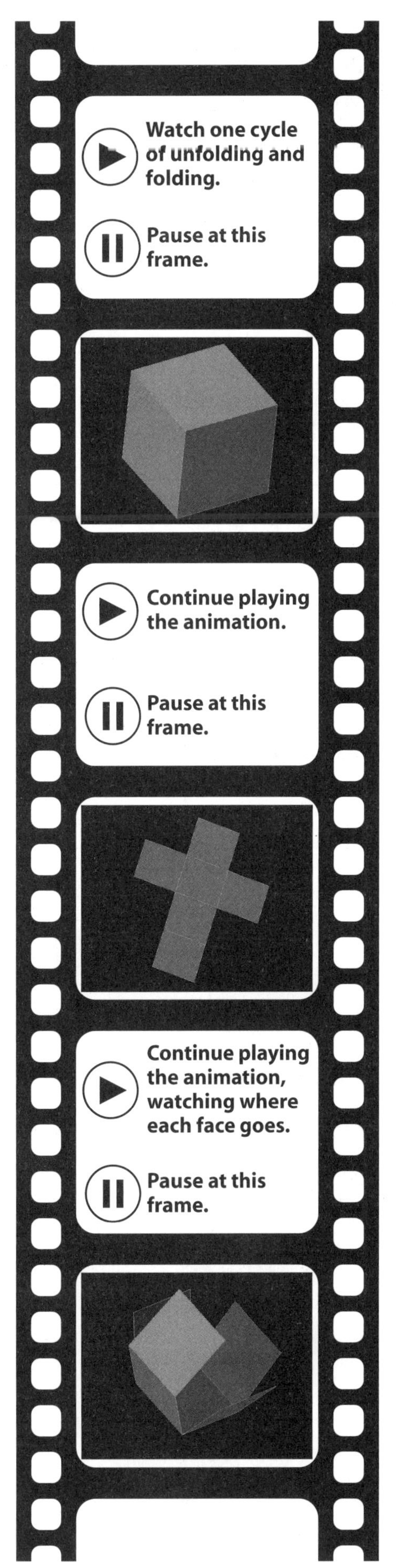

Folding a Net and Unfolding a Cube

How can you fold a cube from a flat piece of paper?

What is the name of this shape?

What shape is each of its faces?

How many square faces does it take to make a cube?

If the center square is the top, identify the bottom and sides.

Did you identify the faces correctly?

How might a net of a rectangular solid be different from the cube's net?

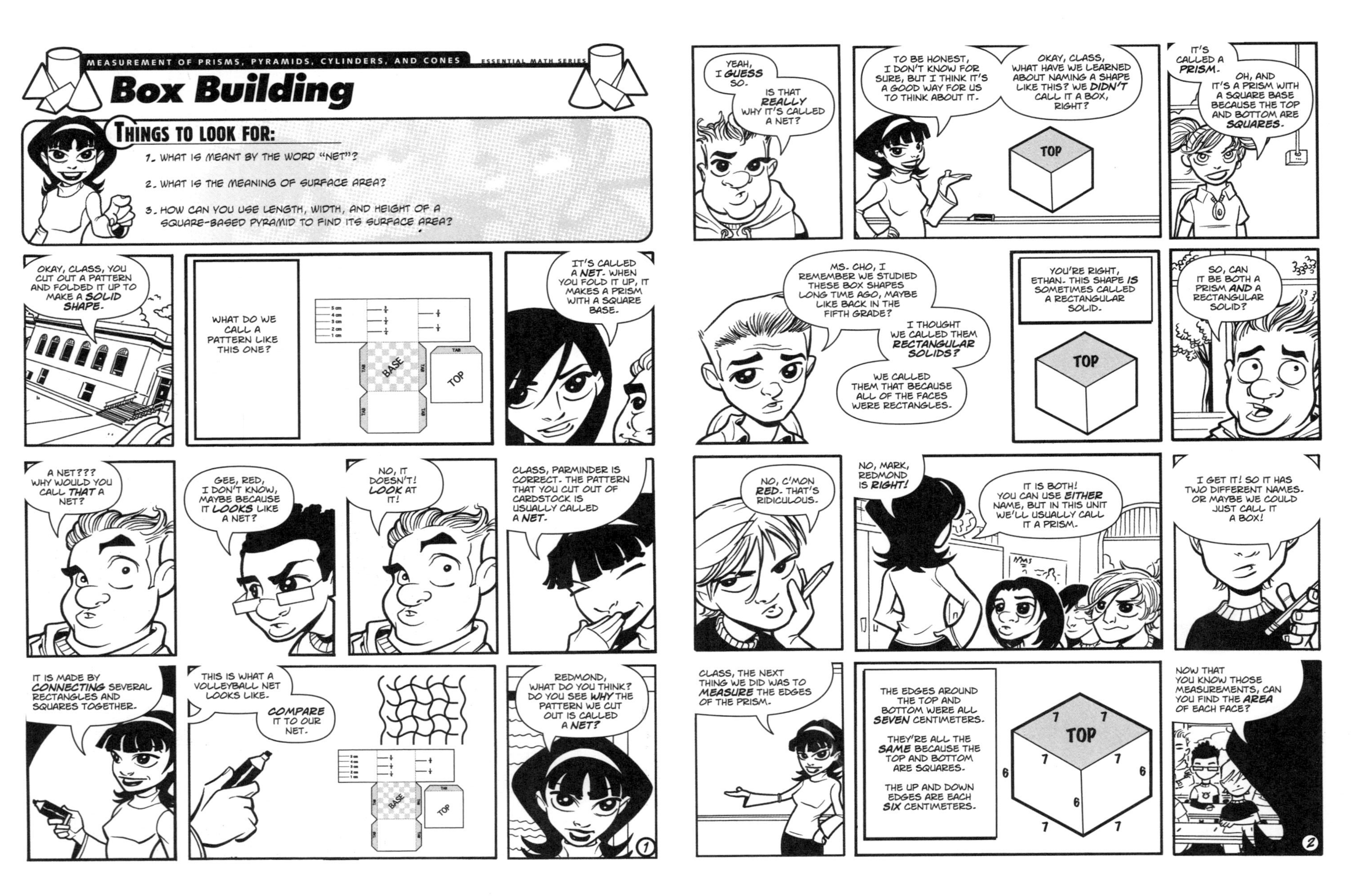
MEASUREMENT OF PRISMS, PYRAMIDS, CYLINDERS, AND CONES
ESSENTIAL MATH SERIES
Box Building
THINGS TO LOOK FOR:
1. WHAT IS MEANT BY THE WORD "NET"?
2. WHAT IS THE MEANING OF SURFACE AREA?
3. HOW CAN YOU USE LENGTH, WIDTH, AND HEIGHT OF A SQUARE-BASED PYRAMID TO FIND ITS SURFACE AREA?
OKAY, CLASS, YOU CUT OUT A PATTERN AND FOLDED IT UP TO MAKE A SOLID SHAPE.
WHAT DO WE CALL A PATTERN LIKE THIS ONE?
BASE
TAB
TOP
IT'S CALLED A NET. WHEN YOU FOLD IT UP, IT MAKES A PRISM WITH A SQUARE BASE.
A NET??? WHY WOULD YOU CALL THAT A NET?
GEE, RED, I DON'T KNOW, MAYBE BECAUSE IT LOOKS LIKE A NET?
NO, IT DOESN'T! LOOK AT IT!
CLASS, PARMINDER IS CORRECT. THE PATTERN THAT YOU CUT OUT OF CARDSTOCK IS USUALLY CALLED A NET.
IT IS MADE BY CONNECTING SEVERAL RECTANGLES AND SQUARES TOGETHER.
THIS IS WHAT A VOLLEYBALL NET LOOKS LIKE.
COMPARE IT TO OUR NET.
BASE
TOP
REDMOND, WHAT DO YOU THINK? DO YOU SEE WHY THE PATTERN WE CUT OUT IS CALLED A NET?
1
YEAH, I GUESS SO.
IS THAT REALLY WHY IT'S CALLED A NET?
TO BE HONEST, I DON'T KNOW FOR SURE, BUT I THINK IT'S A GOOD WAY FOR US TO THINK ABOUT IT.
OKAY, CLASS, WHAT HAVE WE LEARNED ABOUT NAMING A SHAPE LIKE THIS? WE DIDN'T CALL IT A BOX, RIGHT?
TOP
IT'S CALLED A PRISM.
OH, AND IT'S A PRISM WITH A SQUARE BASE BECAUSE THE TOP AND BOTTOM ARE SQUARES.
MS. CHO, I REMEMBER WE STUDIED THESE BOX SHAPES LONG TIME AGO, MAYBE LIKE BACK IN THE FIFTH GRADE?
I THOUGHT WE CALLED THEM RECTANGULAR SOLIDS?
WE CALLED THEM THAT BECAUSE ALL OF THE FACES WERE RECTANGLES.
YOU'RE RIGHT, ETHAN. THIS SHAPE IS SOMETIMES CALLED A RECTANGULAR SOLID.
TOP
SO, CAN IT BE BOTH A PRISM AND A RECTANGULAR SOLID?
NO, C'MON RED. THAT'S RIDICULOUS.
NO, MARK, REDMOND IS RIGHT!
IT IS BOTH! YOU CAN USE EITHER NAME, BUT IN THIS UNIT WE'LL USUALLY CALL IT A PRISM.
I GET IT! SO IT HAS TWO DIFFERENT NAMES. OR MAYBE WE COULD JUST CALL IT A BOX!
CLASS, THE NEXT THING WE DID WAS TO MEASURE THE EDGES OF THE PRISM.
THE EDGES AROUND THE TOP AND BOTTOM WERE ALL SEVEN CENTIMETERS.
THEY'RE ALL THE SAME BECAUSE THE TOP AND BOTTOM ARE SQUARES.
THE UP AND DOWN EDGES ARE EACH SIX CENTIMETERS.
TOP
7
7
7
7
6
6
6
7
7
NOW THAT YOU KNOW THOSE MEASUREMENTS, CAN YOU FIND THE AREA OF EACH FACE?
2

THE TOP AND BOTTOM EACH HAVE AN AREA OF 49 SQUARE CENTIMETERS, WHICH IS 7 TIMES 7.
THE OTHER FOUR FACES ARE RECTANGLES THAT ARE 6 BY 7, SO THE AREA OF EACH OF THOSE RECTANGLES IS 42 SQUARE CENTIMETERS.
OKAY, SO, WHAT DO YOU GET WHEN YOU ADD UP THE AREAS OF THE SIX FACES OF THIS PRISM?
WHEN YOU ADD THEM ALL UP, YOU GET 266.
266 WHAT? WHAT ARE THE AREA UNITS?
OH, YEAH. THEY'RE SQUARE CENTIMETERS. THE TOTAL AREA IS 266 SQUARE CENTIMETERS.
CLASS, WE CALL THAT THE SURFACE AREA OF THE PRISM.
EACH FACE OF THE PRISM IS A FLAT SURFACE, AND ALL OF THESE FACES TOGETHER ARE THE SURFACE OF THE PRISM.
WHEN YOU ADD UP THE AREAS OF THESE SIX FACES, THAT'S THE AREA OF THE SURFACE OF THE PRISM, OR THE SURFACE AREA.
YOU SURE SAID THE WORD SURFACE A LOT.
YOU KNOW, REDMOND, I DID THAT ON PURPOSE.
WE'RE GOING TO BE USING THIS IDEA OF SURFACE AREA OVER AND OVER AGAIN IN THIS UNIT. I WANT TO MAKE SURE THAT YOU KNOW WHAT IT MEANS.
surface area
LET'S FIND THE SURFACE AREA OF ONE MORE PRISM. NOTICE THAT THE BASES ARE RECTANGLES.
5cm 4cm 4cm 5cm 7cm 7cm 7cm 4cm 5cm
THE TOP AND BOTTOM BOTH HAVE AN AREA OF 20, ANOTHER TWO OF THE FACES EACH HAS AN AREA OF 35, AND THE OTHER TWO EACH HAS AN AREA OF 28.
WHEN YOU ADD THEM UP, YOU GET 166. SO, THE SURFACE AREA IS 166 SQUARE CENTIMETERS.
20 sq. cm
35 sq. cm
28 sq. cm
20 20 28 28 35 35 166
EVERYBODY GOT IT?
GREAT JOB, CLASS!

How do you determine how many centimeter cubes it takes to fill a rectangular solid (prism)?

Filling boxes with layers of cubes illustrates that the area of the base as the number of cubes in a layer. Multiplying the number of cubes in a layer by the number of layers gives the volume of the box (rectangular prism). By using the same box made to find surface area in the previous activity, the difference between the measures of surface area and volume is understood.

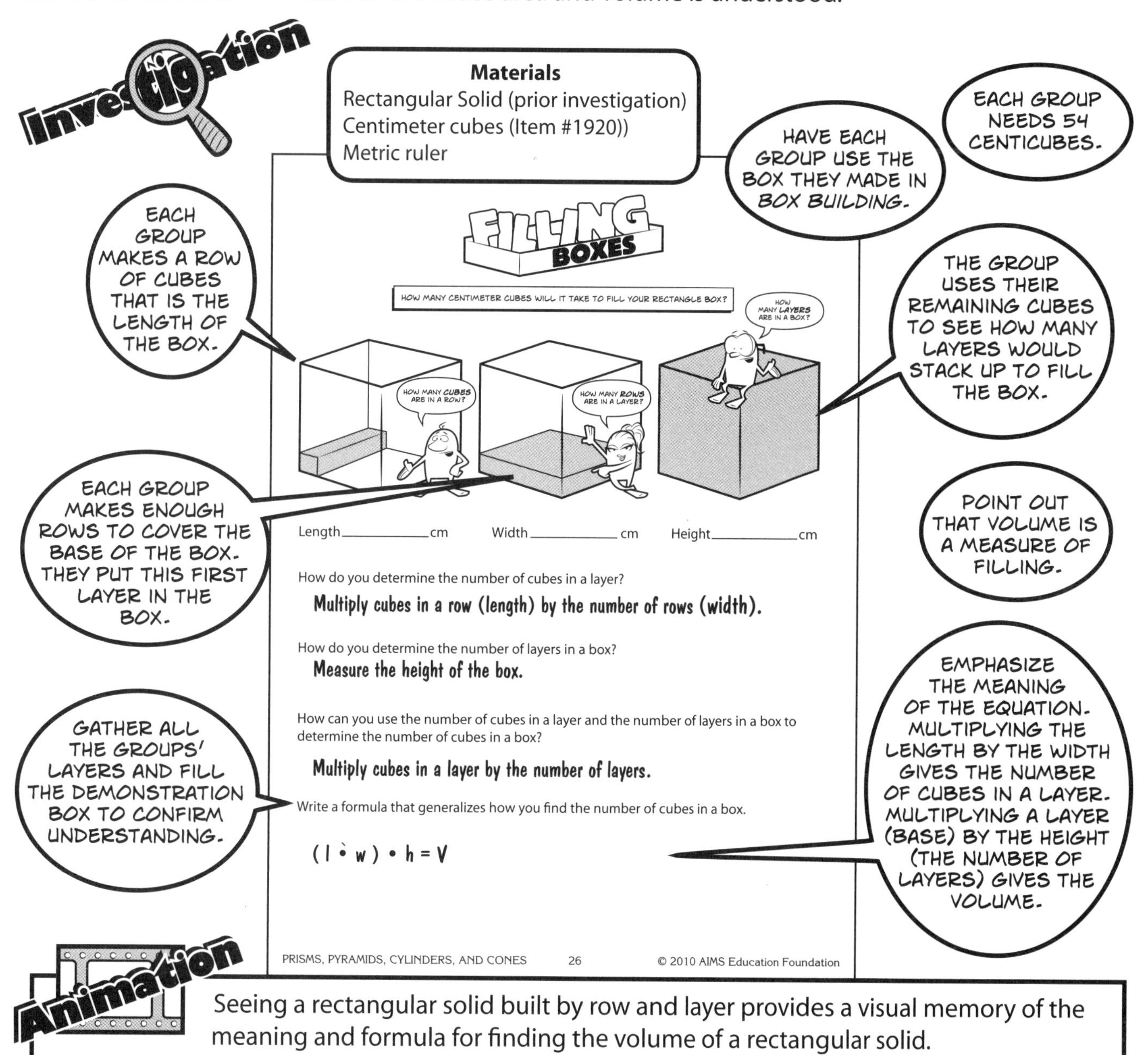

Seeing a rectangular solid built by row and layer provides a visual memory of the meaning and formula for finding the volume of a rectangular solid.

Comics

Emphasizes that volume is a measure of filling and is reported in cubic units. It also helps students understand the formulas for finding the volume of a rectangular-based prism.

HOW MANY CENTIMETER CUBES WILL IT TAKE TO FILL YOUR RECTANGLE BOX?

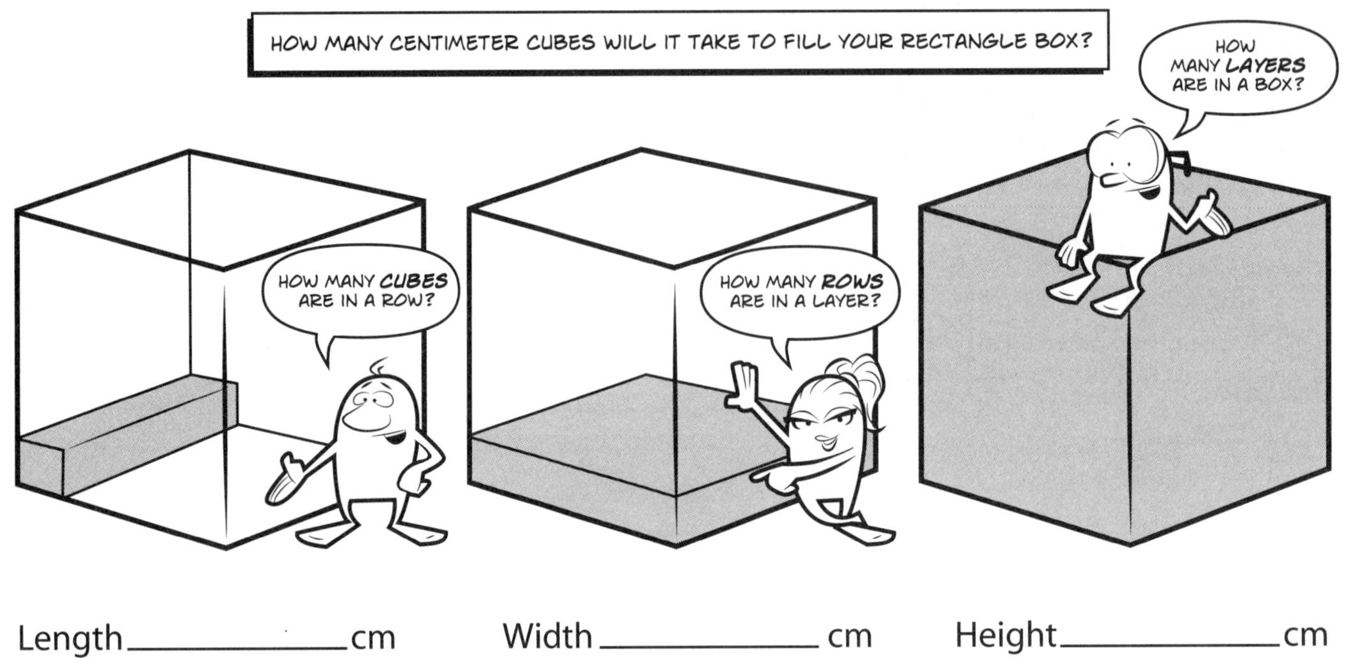

Length ____________ cm Width ____________ cm Height ____________ cm

How do you determine the number of cubes in a layer?

How do you determine the number of layers in a box?

How can you use the number of cubes in a layer and the number of layers in a box to determine the number of cubes in a box?

Write a formula that generalizes how you find the number of cubes in a box.

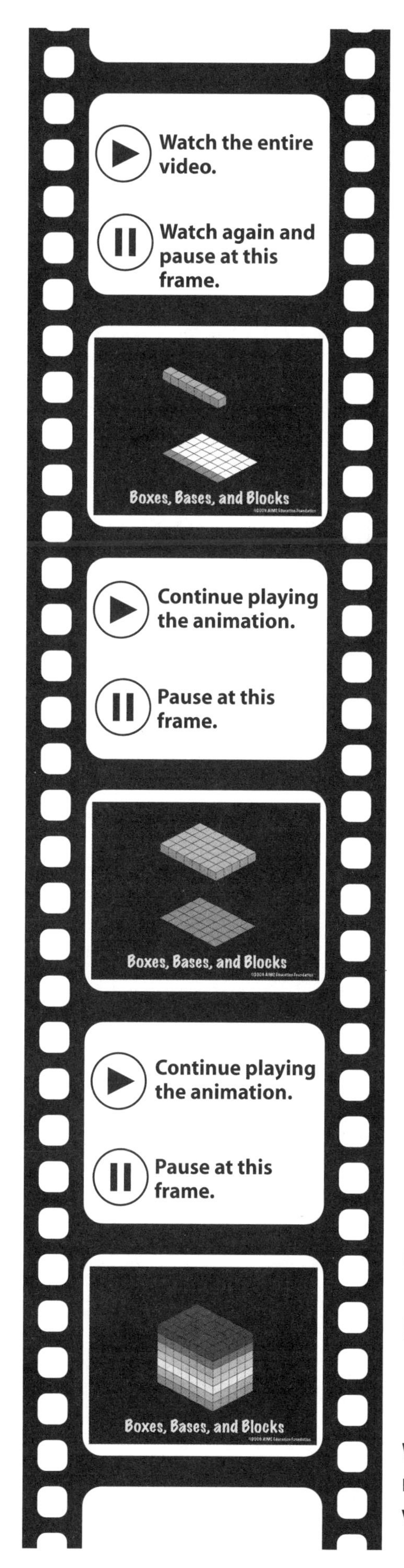

Boxes, Bases, and Blocks

How does the formula for the volume of a box describe what fills the box?

How many units does it take to cover one row of the base?

What dimension of the rectangular base does this represent?

How many rows does it take to cover the rectangular base?

What does multiplying the number of cubes in a row by the number of rows tell you about the base?

How many layers are in this rectangular solid?

How do you determine the number of cubes in this rectangular solid?

Write a formula that calculates the number of cubes in a rectangular solid and explain how the formula relates to what is seen in the animation.

MEASUREMENT OF PRISMS, PYRAMIDS, CYLINDERS, AND CONES
ESSENTIAL MATH SERIES
Filling Boxes
THINGS TO LOOK FOR:
1. WHY ARE THE UNITS USED TO MEASURE VOLUME CALLED CUBIC UNITS?
2. HOW DOES KNOWING THE AREA OF THE BASE HELP YOU TO FIND THE VOLUME OF A PRISM?
3. HOW DO YOU KNOW THAT THE TWO FORMULAS, V = B • h AND V = l • w • h WILL BOTH GIVE YOU THE VOLUME OF A SQUARE-BASED PRISM?
IN THE LAST ACTIVITY YOU MADE A PRISM WITH A SQUARE BASE AND THEN FOUND ITS SURFACE AREA.
IN THIS ACTIVITY YOU FOUND THE VOLUME OF THAT SAME PRISM.
HOW DO WE MEASURE VOLUME?
TOP
YOU USE CUBES. YOU HAVE TO FIND OUT HOW MANY CUBES IT TAKES TO FILL THE PRISM.
YEAH, AND WE COULDN'T FILL IT BY JUST POURING CUBES INTO THE BOX. WE HAD TO FILL THEM IN LAYERS.
SO, WHY WAS THAT? WHY DID WE FILL THE PRISM WITH LAYERS OF CUBES?
UH, IS IT BECAUSE WE WANTED TO GET AS MANY IN THERE AS WE COULD?
OF COURSE IT IS, RED. THINK ABOUT IT. IF YOU COMPLETELY FILL THE PRISM A LAYER AT A TIME, THERE CAN'T BE ANY EMPTY SPACES.
THAT WAY YOU FIND OUT HOW MANY CUBES IT TAKES TO FILL IT LEVEL FULL.
YES. SO, THE VOLUME OF A PRISM IS HOW MANY CUBES IT TAKES TO FILL IT.
CLASS, A GOOD WAY TO REMEMBER WHAT VOLUME MEANS IS TO THINK OF IT AS A MEASURE OF FILLING.
BUT, MS. CHO, WE DIDN'T FILL THE PRISM UNTIL CLEAR AT THE END OF THE ACTIVITY!
1
YEAH, BUT WE FIGURED OUT HOW MANY IT WOULD TAKE TO FILL IT BEFORE WE DID IT.
OKAY, GUYS, GOOD.
SO, HOW DID WE FIGURE OUT HOW MANY CUBES IT WOULD TAKE?
WELL, FIRST WE FILLED IN THE BOTTOM LAYER.
THAT TOOK 49 CUBES.
THEN WE STACKED UP SOME CUBES TO SEE HOW MANY LAYERS IT WOULD TAKE TO FILL IT.
IT TAKES SIX LAYERS, SO THAT'S 6 TIMES 49 CUBES TO FILL THE PRISM.
RIGHT, IT TAKES 294 OF THOSE CUBES TO FILL IT.
OKAY, CLASS, SO WHEN YOU COMBINED YOUR CUBES WITH LAYERS OF CUBES FROM OTHER GROUPS AND FILLED ONE OF THE BOXES, IT LOOKED LIKE THIS, RIGHT?
BY THE WAY, WHAT DO YOU CALL THESE CUBES?
I KNOW WHAT THEY ARE!
THEY'RE CENTIMETER CUBES. YOU SAID WE SHOULD CALL THEM CUBIC CENTIMETERS.
THAT MEANS THE VOLUME OF THIS PRISM IS 294 CUBIC CENTIMENTERS, RIGHT?
MS. CHO, WE DIDN'T REALLY HAVE TO PUT CUBES IN THE PRISM TO KNOW HOW MANY IT WOULD TAKE TO MAKE ONE LAYER.
WE DIDN'T?? HOW ELSE WOULD WE KNOW?
ALL YOU REALLY NEED TO KNOW IS THE AREA OF THE BOTTOM OF THE PRISM.
THE BOTTOM IS A SQUARE THAT'S 7 BY 7. THE SQUARES ARE EVEN DRAWN ON THE BOTTOM FACE. IF YOU PUT A CUBE ON ONE OF THOSE SQUARES, IT EXACTLY FITS. THAT MEANS YOU CAN PUT A CUBE ON EVERY SQUARE.
2

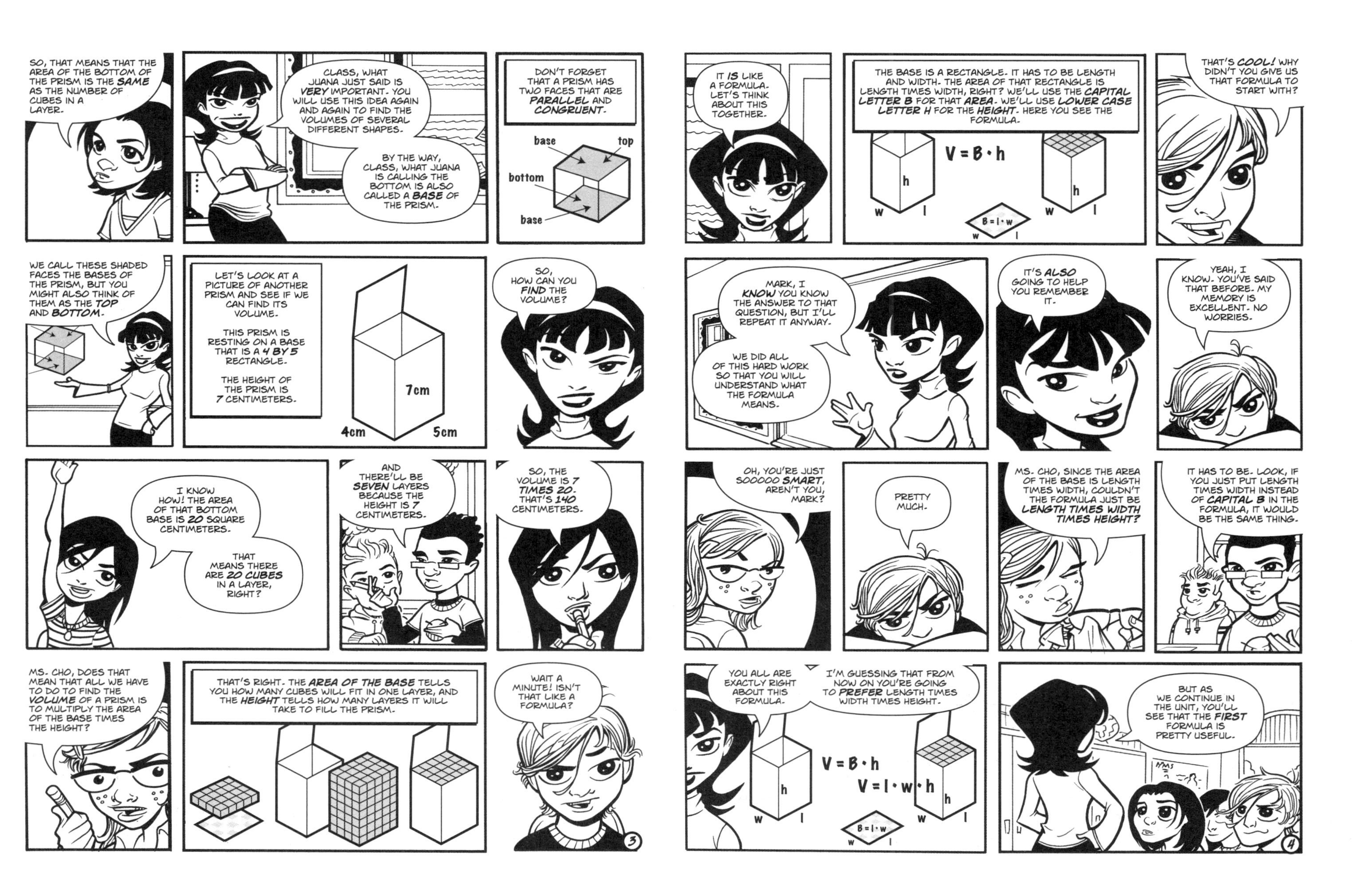
SO, THAT MEANS THAT THE AREA OF THE BOTTOM OF THE PRISM IS THE SAME AS THE NUMBER OF CUBES IN A LAYER.
CLASS, WHAT JUANA JUST SAID IS VERY IMPORTANT. YOU WILL USE THIS IDEA AGAIN AND AGAIN TO FIND THE VOLUMES OF SEVERAL DIFFERENT SHAPES.
BY THE WAY, CLASS, WHAT JUANA IS CALLING THE BOTTOM IS ALSO CALLED A BASE OF THE PRISM.
DON'T FORGET THAT A PRISM HAS TWO FACES THAT ARE PARALLEL AND CONGRUENT.
base
top
bottom
base
WE CALL THESE SHADED FACES THE BASES OF THE PRISM, BUT YOU MIGHT ALSO THINK OF THEM AS THE TOP AND BOTTOM.
LET'S LOOK AT A PICTURE OF ANOTHER PRISM AND SEE IF WE CAN FIND ITS VOLUME.
THIS PRISM IS RESTING ON A BASE THAT IS A 4 BY 5 RECTANGLE.
THE HEIGHT OF THE PRISM IS 7 CENTIMETERS.
7cm
4cm
5cm
SO, HOW CAN YOU FIND THE VOLUME?
I KNOW HOW! THE AREA OF THAT BOTTOM BASE IS 20 SQUARE CENTIMETERS.
THAT MEANS THERE ARE 20 CUBES IN A LAYER, RIGHT?
AND THERE'LL BE SEVEN LAYERS BECAUSE THE HEIGHT IS 7 CENTIMETERS.
SO, THE VOLUME IS 7 TIMES 20. THAT'S 140 CENTIMETERS.
MS. CHO, DOES THAT MEAN THAT ALL WE HAVE TO DO TO FIND THE VOLUME OF A PRISM IS TO MULTIPLY THE AREA OF THE BASE TIMES THE HEIGHT?
THAT'S RIGHT. THE AREA OF THE BASE TELLS YOU HOW MANY CUBES WILL FIT IN ONE LAYER, AND THE HEIGHT TELLS HOW MANY LAYERS IT WILL TAKE TO FILL THE PRISM.
WAIT A MINUTE! ISN'T THAT LIKE A FORMULA?
3
IT IS LIKE A FORMULA. LET'S THINK ABOUT THIS TOGETHER.
THE BASE IS A RECTANGLE. IT HAS TO BE LENGTH AND WIDTH. THE AREA OF THAT RECTANGLE IS LENGTH TIMES WIDTH, RIGHT? WE'LL USE THE CAPITAL LETTER B FOR THAT AREA. WE'LL USE LOWER CASE LETTER H FOR THE HEIGHT. HERE YOU SEE THE FORMULA.
V = B • h
h
w
l
B = l • w
THAT'S COOL! WHY DIDN'T YOU GIVE US THAT FORMULA TO START WITH?
MARK, I KNOW YOU KNOW THE ANSWER TO THAT QUESTION, BUT I'LL REPEAT IT ANYWAY.
WE DID ALL OF THIS HARD WORK SO THAT YOU WILL UNDERSTAND WHAT THE FORMULA MEANS.
IT'S ALSO GOING TO HELP YOU REMEMBER IT.
YEAH, I KNOW. YOU'VE SAID THAT BEFORE. MY MEMORY IS EXCELLENT. NO WORRIES.
OH, YOU'RE JUST SOOOOO SMART, AREN'T YOU, MARK?
PRETTY MUCH.
MS. CHO, SINCE THE AREA OF THE BASE IS LENGTH TIMES WIDTH, COULDN'T THE FORMULA JUST BE LENGTH TIMES WIDTH TIMES HEIGHT?
IT HAS TO BE. LOOK, IF YOU JUST PUT LENGTH TIMES WIDTH INSTEAD OF CAPITAL B IN THE FORMULA, IT WOULD BE THE SAME THING.
YOU ALL ARE EXACTLY RIGHT ABOUT THIS FORMULA.
I'M GUESSING THAT FROM NOW ON YOU'RE GOING TO PREFER LENGTH TIMES WIDTH TIMES HEIGHT.
V = B • h
V = l • w • h
B = l • w
BUT AS WE CONTINUE IN THE UNIT, YOU'LL SEE THAT THE FIRST FORMULA IS PRETTY USEFUL.
4

Box Building and Filling — Practice

What is the surface area and volume of each rectangular solid?

THROUGHOUT THIS EXPERIENCE, SURFACE AREA AS A MEASURE OF COVERING AND VOLUME AS A MEASURE OF FILLING SHOULD BE EMPHASIZED.

THE PAGE PROVIDES THREE LEVELS OF ABSTRACTIONS FOR DETERMINING SURFACE AREA AND VOLUME.

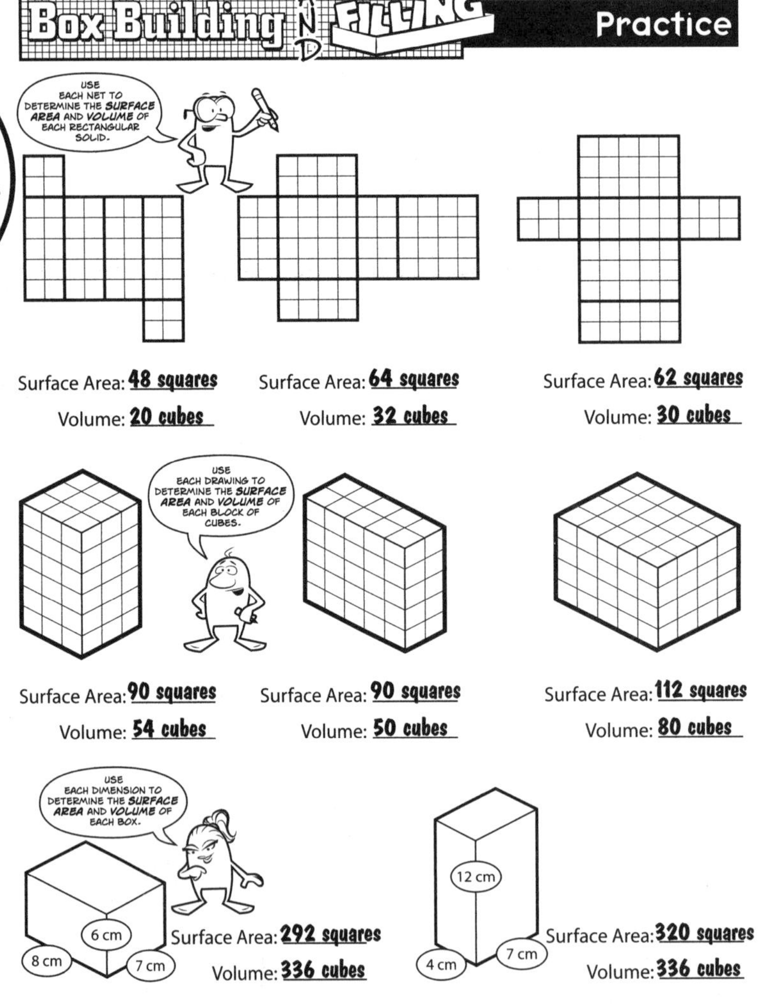

Box Building and Filling — Practice

USE EACH NET TO DETERMINE THE *SURFACE AREA* AND *VOLUME* OF EACH RECTANGULAR SOLID.

Surface Area: 48 squares
Volume: 20 cubes

Surface Area: 64 squares
Volume: 32 cubes

Surface Area: 62 squares
Volume: 30 cubes

USE EACH DRAWING TO DETERMINE THE *SURFACE AREA* AND *VOLUME* OF EACH BLOCK OF CUBES.

Surface Area: 90 squares
Volume: 54 cubes

Surface Area: 90 squares
Volume: 50 cubes

Surface Area: 112 squares
Volume: 80 cubes

USE EACH DIMENSION TO DETERMINE THE *SURFACE AREA* AND *VOLUME* OF EACH BOX.

8 cm, 6 cm, 7 cm
Surface Area: 292 squares
Volume: 336 cubes

12 cm, 4 cm, 7 cm
Surface Area: 320 squares
Volume: 336 cubes

PRISMS, PYRAMIDS, CYLINDERS, AND CONES 31 © 2010 AIMS Education Foundation

AS STUDENTS WORK DOWN THE PAGE, THE ILLUSTRATIONS BECOME MORE ABSTRACT.

SURFACE AREA IS REPORTED IN SQUARES—A UNIT OF TWO DIMENSIONS (LENGTH AND WIDTH).

VOLUME IS REPORTED IN CUBES—A UNIT OF THREE DIMENSIONS (LENGTH, WIDTH, AND HEIGHT).

Box Building and Filling Practice

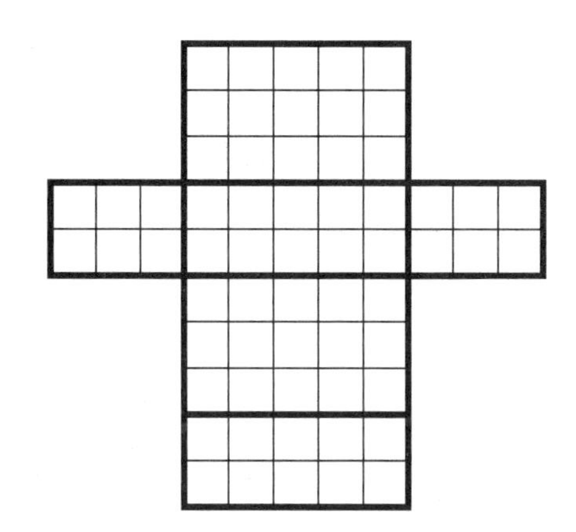

Surface Area: ________ Surface Area: ________ Surface Area: ________

Volume: ________ Volume: ________ Volume: ________

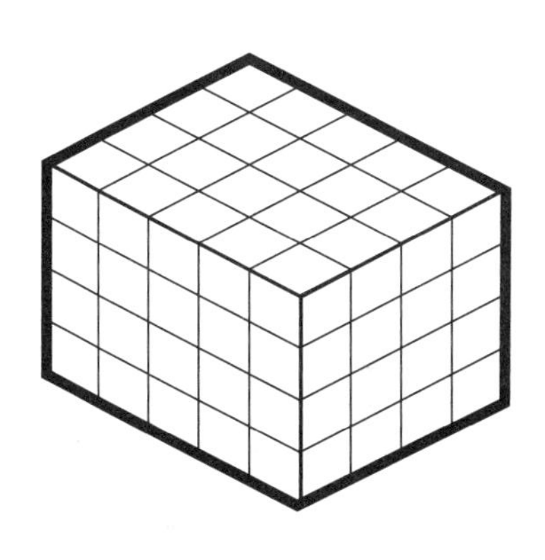

Surface Area: ________ Surface Area: ________ Surface Area: ________

Volume: ________ Volume: ________ Volume: ________

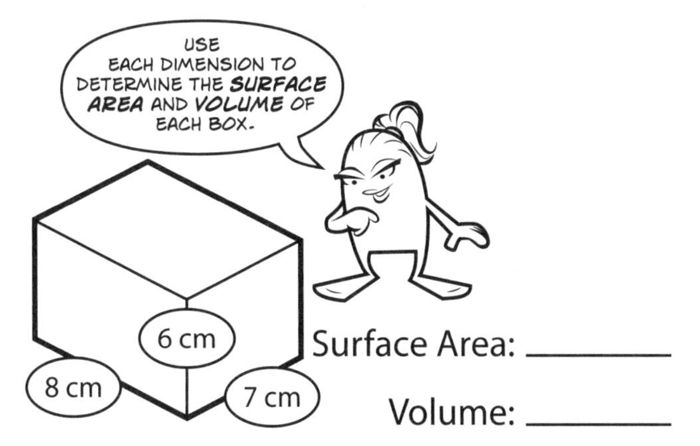

Surface Area: ________

Volume: ________

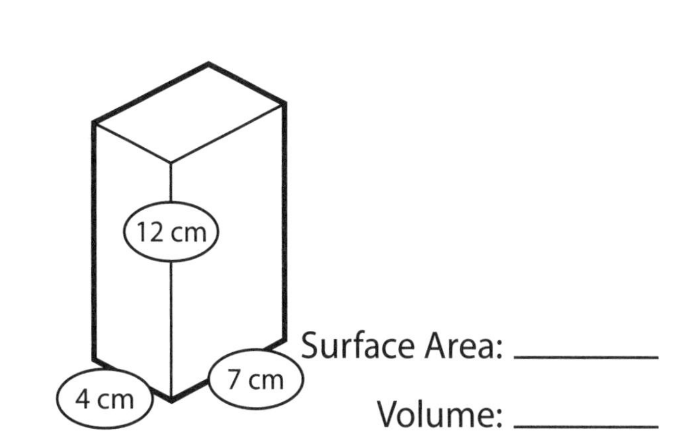

Surface Area: ________

Volume: ________

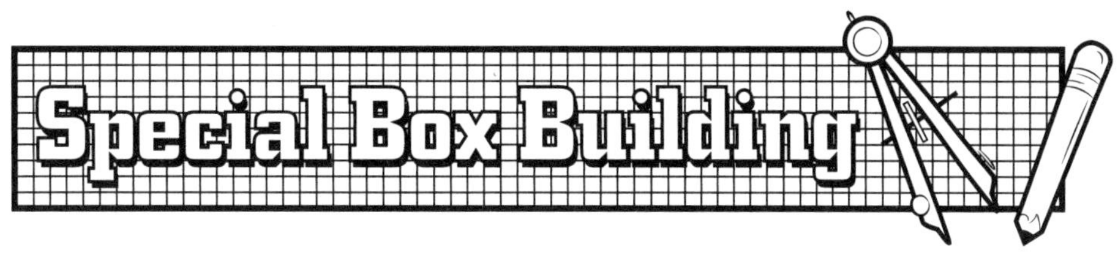

How do you determine how much cardboard it takes to build a box in the shape of a prism or cylinder?

Building a box from a net is an opportunity to identify the shapes used to make all the surfaces of the solid. Seeing the net reinforces the idea of surface area as a measure of covering and a sum of all the shapes on the surfaces surrounding the solid.

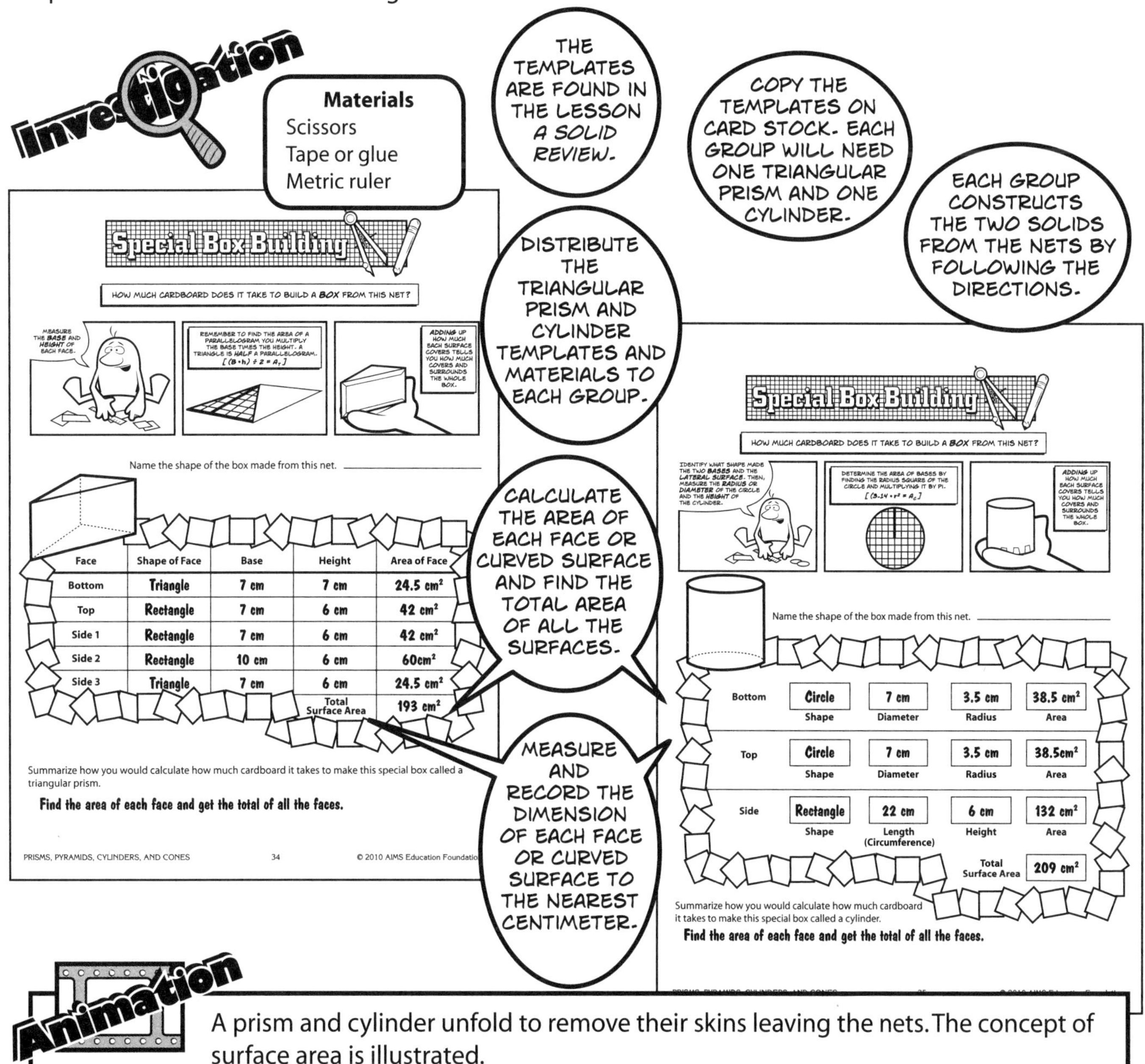

Animation

A prism and cylinder unfold to remove their skins leaving the nets. The concept of surface area is illustrated.

Comics

Reviews formulas for finding the area of a triangle and circle, then progresses to summing the areas of all component parts to determine surface area.

HOW MUCH CARDBOARD DOES IT TAKE TO BUILD A ***BOX*** FROM THIS NET?

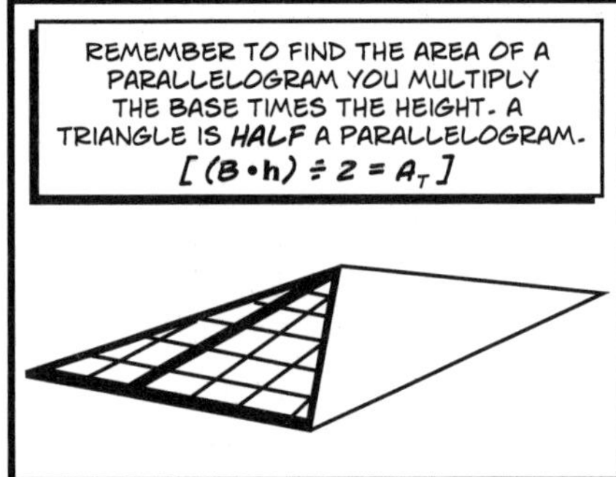

Name the shape of the box made from this net. ______________________

Face	Shape of Face	Base	Height	Area of Face
Bottom				
Top				
Side 1				
Side 2				
Side 3				
			Total Surface Area	

Summarize how you would calculate how much cardboard it takes to make this special box called a triangular prism.

Special Box Building

HOW MUCH CARDBOARD DOES IT TAKE TO BUILD A ***BOX*** FROM THIS NET?

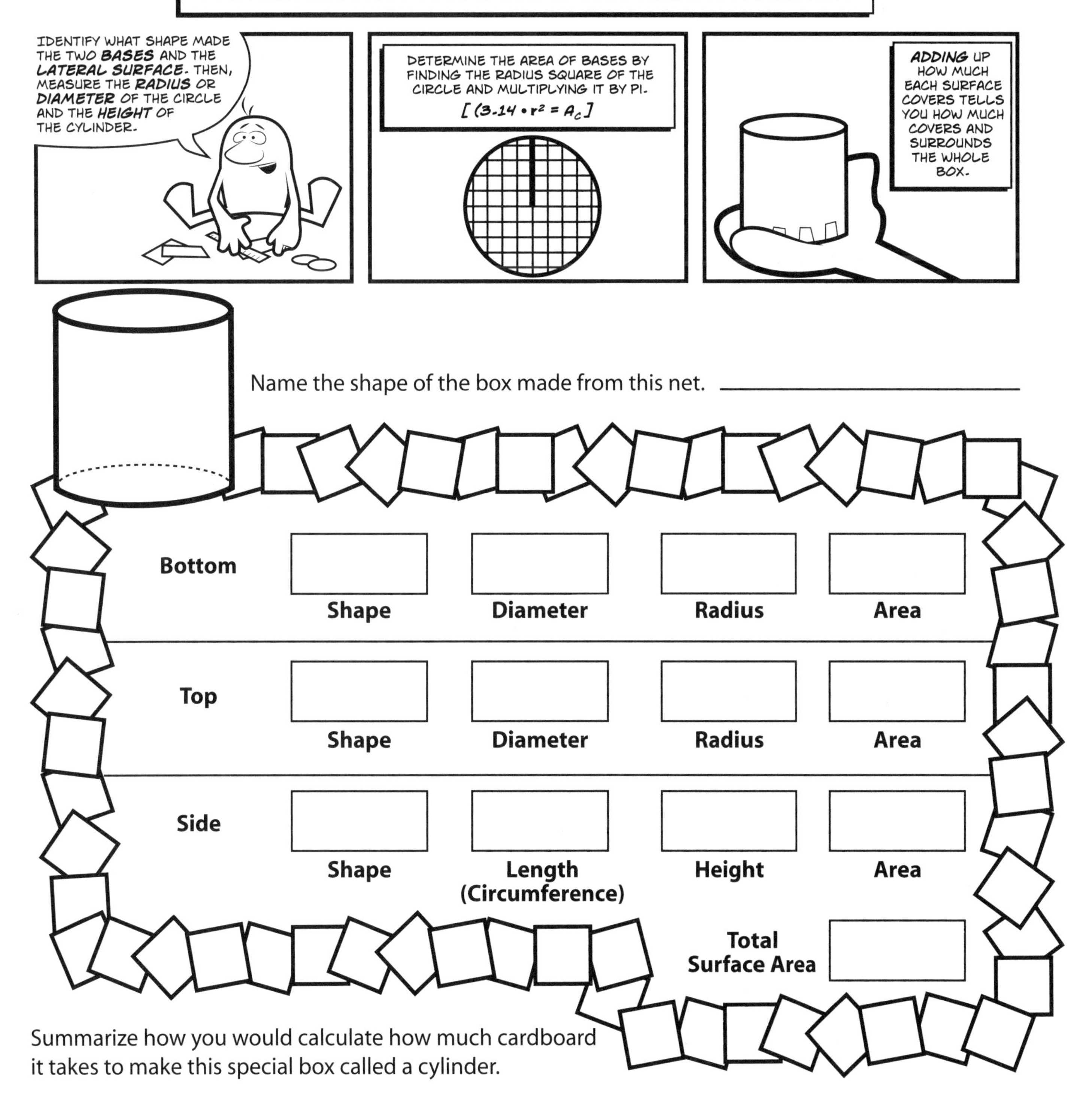

Name the shape of the box made from this net. ____________________

Bottom	**Shape**	**Diameter**	**Radius**	**Area**
Top	**Shape**	**Diameter**	**Radius**	**Area**
Side	**Shape**	**Length (Circumference)**	**Height**	**Area**
			Total Surface Area	

Summarize how you would calculate how much cardboard it takes to make this special box called a cylinder.

Unfolding Prisms and Cylinders

How do you find the surface area of prisms and cylinders?

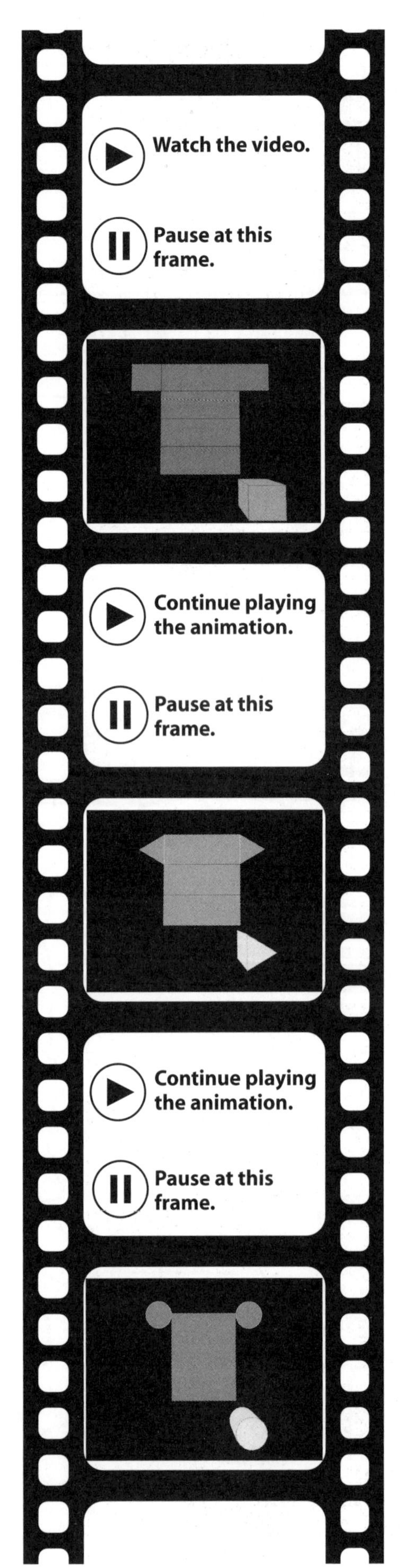

Identify the shapes needed to make this solid by outlining each face or surface on the net.

How can you use the shapes you identified to find the surface area of this prism?

Identify the shapes needed to make this solid by outlining each face or surface on the net.

How can you use the shapes you identified to find the surface area of this prism?

Identify the shapes needed to make this solid by outlining each face or surface on the net.

How can you use the shapes you identified to find the surface area of this cylinder?

Summarize how you find the surface area of a prism or cylinder.

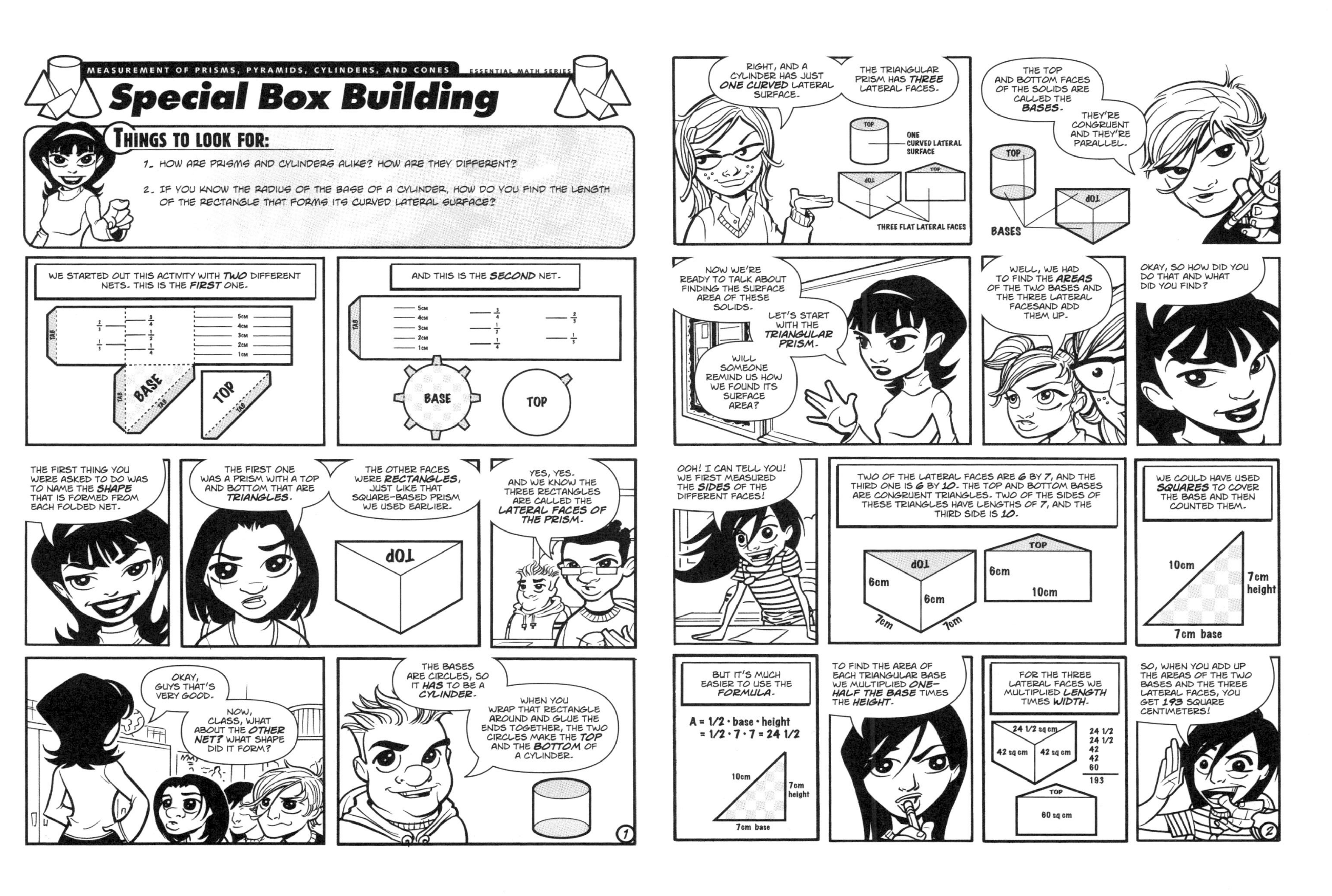
MEASUREMENT OF PRISMS, PYRAMIDS, CYLINDERS, AND CONES
ESSENTIAL MATH SERIES
Special Box Building
THINGS TO LOOK FOR:
1. HOW ARE PRISMS AND CYLINDERS ALIKE? HOW ARE THEY DIFFERENT?
2. IF YOU KNOW THE RADIUS OF THE BASE OF A CYLINDER, HOW DO YOU FIND THE LENGTH OF THE RECTANGLE THAT FORMS ITS CURVED LATERAL SURFACE?
WE STARTED OUT THIS ACTIVITY WITH TWO DIFFERENT NETS. THIS IS THE FIRST ONE.
TAB
5CM
4CM
3CM
2CM
1CM
BASE
TOP
AND THIS IS THE SECOND NET.
BASE
TOP
THE FIRST THING YOU WERE ASKED TO DO WAS TO NAME THE SHAPE THAT IS FORMED FROM EACH FOLDED NET.
THE FIRST ONE WAS A PRISM WITH A TOP AND BOTTOM THAT ARE TRIANGLES.
THE OTHER FACES WERE RECTANGLES, JUST LIKE THAT SQUARE-BASED PRISM WE USED EARLIER.
TOP
YES, YES. AND WE KNOW THE THREE RECTANGLES ARE CALLED THE LATERAL FACES OF THE PRISM.
OKAY, GUYS THAT'S VERY GOOD.
NOW, CLASS, WHAT ABOUT THE OTHER NET? WHAT SHAPE DID IT FORM?
THE BASES ARE CIRCLES, SO IT HAS TO BE A CYLINDER.
WHEN YOU WRAP THAT RECTANGLE AROUND AND GLUE THE ENDS TOGETHER, THE TWO CIRCLES MAKE THE TOP AND THE BOTTOM OF A CYLINDER.
1
RIGHT, AND A CYLINDER HAS JUST ONE CURVED LATERAL SURFACE.
THE TRIANGULAR PRISM HAS THREE LATERAL FACES.
TOP
ONE CURVED LATERAL SURFACE
THREE FLAT LATERAL FACES
THE TOP AND BOTTOM FACES OF THE SOLIDS ARE CALLED THE BASES.
THEY'RE CONGRUENT AND THEY'RE PARALLEL.
TOP
BASES
NOW WE'RE READY TO TALK ABOUT FINDING THE SURFACE AREA OF THESE SOLIDS.
LET'S START WITH THE TRIANGULAR PRISM.
WILL SOMEONE REMIND US HOW WE FOUND ITS SURFACE AREA?
WELL, WE HAD TO FIND THE AREAS OF THE TWO BASES AND THE THREE LATERAL FACESAND ADD THEM UP.
OKAY, SO HOW DID YOU DO THAT AND WHAT DID YOU FIND?
OOH! I CAN TELL YOU! WE FIRST MEASURED THE SIDES OF THE DIFFERENT FACES!
TWO OF THE LATERAL FACES ARE 6 BY 7, AND THE THIRD ONE IS 6 BY 10. THE TOP AND BOTTOM BASES ARE CONGRUENT TRIANGLES. TWO OF THE SIDES OF THESE TRIANGLES HAVE LENGTHS OF 7, AND THE THIRD SIDE IS 10.
TOP
6cm
6cm
7cm
7cm
6cm
10cm
WE COULD HAVE USED SQUARES TO COVER THE BASE AND THEN COUNTED THEM.
10cm
7cm height
7cm base
BUT IT'S MUCH EASIER TO USE THE FORMULA.
A = 1/2 · base · height
= 1/2 · 7 · 7 = 24 1/2
10cm
7cm height
7cm base
TO FIND THE AREA OF EACH TRIANGULAR BASE WE MULTIPLIED ONE-HALF THE BASE TIMES THE HEIGHT.
FOR THE THREE LATERAL FACES WE MULTIPLIED LENGTH TIMES WIDTH.
24 1/2 sq cm
42 sq cm
42 sq cm
60 sq cm
24 1/2
24 1/2
42
42
60
193
SO, WHEN YOU ADD UP THE AREAS OF THE TWO BASES AND THE THREE LATERAL FACES, YOU GET 193 SQUARE CENTIMETERS!
2

THAT WAS VERY WELL DONE, PARMINDER.
FINDING THE SURFACE AREA OF THE CYLINDER WAS HARDER.
THE BASES ARE CIRCLES, SO WE HAD TO REMEMBER HOW TO FIND THE AREA OF A CIRCLE.
THEN WE HAD TO FIGURE OUT HOW TO FIND THE AREA OF THAT LATERAL SURFACE.
TOP
ONCE WE ADDED UP THE AREAS OF THOSE PARTS, WE KNEW THE SURFACE AREA OF THE CYLINDER.
EXCELLENT. SO, TELL US HOW YOU DID IT.
WELL, I FIRST FOUND THE AREA OF THE TOP, AND THAT WAS THE SAME AS THE AREA OF THE BOTTOM.
THE CIRCLES HAD A DIAMETER OF 7 CENTIMETERS. WITH THAT, I COULD USE THE FORMULA TO FIND THE AREA.
THE FORUMLA IS PI TIMES THE RADIUS SQUARED.
YOU REVIEWED THAT WITH US.
IF THE DIAMETER IS 7, THEN THE RADIUS HAS TO BE 3 1/2.
I CHANGED 3 1/2 TO 3.5 TO MAKE IT EASIER.
diameter is 7 cm
radius is 3 1/2 or 3.5
TOP
$A = \pi \cdot r^2$
I PUT 3.14 IN PLACE OF PI, AND THEN I USED A CALCULATOR TO FIND THE AREA. IT WAS 38.47 SQUARE CENTIMENTERS.
$A = \pi \cdot r^2$
$A = 3.14 \cdot (3.5)^2$
$A = 3.14 \cdot 12.25$
$A = 38.47$ sq cm
THAT'S RIGHT. THAT'S THE AREA OF THE BASE. HOW ABOUT IF WE ROUND IT UP TO 38.5?
CLASS, REMEMBER THAT THE 38.5 IS HOW MANY SQUARES IT TAKES TO COVER THE CIRCLE. THAT'S WHAT THE FORMULA HELPS YOU FIND OUT.
IF YOU LOOK AT THE BOTTOM BASE YOU CAN SEE THE SQUARES THAT IT TAKES TO COVER THE CIRCLE.
BASE
YOU CAN SEE THAT A LOT OF THE SQUARES HAD TO BE CUT IN PIECES TO FIT IN THE CIRCLE.
THAT'S WHY IT'S GOOD TO HAVE A FORMULA. IT WOULD BE A LOT OF WORK TO TRY TO COUNT THE SQUARES.
3
OKAY, CLASS, WE FOUND THE AREA OF ONE OTHER PART OF THE CYLINDER, THE CURVED SURFACE THAT WRAPS AROUND THESE TWO BASES.
TOP
YEAH, I STILL DON'T GET HOW TO DO THAT. WE DON'T HAVE A FORMULA FOR THAT, DO WE?
IT WOULD BE EASIEST TO FIND THE AREA OF THAT PIECE BEFORE WE WRAPPED IT AROUND TO MAKE THE CYLINDER.
BEFORE WE MADE IT INTO A CYLINDER IT WAS JUST A RECTANGLE. WE STILL HAD ONE OF THE NETS, SO I MEASURED IT. THE WIDTH WAS 6 CM, THAT'S THE SAME AS THE HEIGHT OF THE CYLINDER. AND THE LENGTH WAS 22 CM, WITHOUT THE TAB.
YEAH, BUT THAT'S NOT HOW THE REST OF US DID IT. HOW DID WE FIGURE IT OUT WITHOUT THE NET?
WELL, RED, HOW DO YOU SUPPOSE THE PERSON WHO DREW UP THIS NET FIGURED OUT HOW LONG TO MAKE THE RECTANGLE?
BASE
TOP
EASY. THE RECTANGLE HAS TO BE JUST LONG ENOUGH TO WRAP AROUND THE CIRCLE. THE LENGTH WOULD BE THE SAME AS THE CIRCUMFERENCE OF THE CIRCLE.
THE FORMULA FOR THE CIRCUMFERENCE IS PI TIMES THE DIAMETER. SO, THE DIAMETER IS 7, AND 3.14 TIMES 7 IS 21.98. I DID IT ON MY CALCULATOR. THAT'S ALMOST 22 CENTIMETERS.
$C = \pi \cdot d$
$= 3.14 \cdot 7$ cm
$= 22.98$ cm
22 cm
SO, IF YOU UNWRAP THAT LATERAL SURFACE OF A CYLINDER IT WOULD ALWAYS MAKE A RECTANGLE, RIGHT?
AND THE LENGTH OF THAT RECTANGLE IS THE CIRCUMFERENCE OF THE CYLINDER, AND THE WIDTH IS ITS HEIGHT.
OKAY, SO WHAT IS THE AREA OF THIS CURVED SURFACE OF OUR CYLINDER?
THE AREA OF THE RECTANGLE IS 6 TIMES 22 OR 132 SQUARE CENTIMETERS.
UR-HURM!
THE SURFACE AREA OF THE CYLINDER IS WHAT YOU GET WHEN YOU ADD UP THE AREAS OF THE TWO BASES AND THE CURVED SURFACE PART.
THAT'S 77 PLUS 132.
SO...THE TOTAL SURFACE AREA IS 209 SQUARE CENTIMETERS.
38.5 sq cm
132 sq cm
38.5 sq cm
132
38.5
38.5
209 sq cm
4

How do you determine how many centimeter cubes it takes to fill a triangular prism or a cylinder?

Filling boxes with layers of cubes illustrates the area of the base as the number of cubes in a layer. By multiplying the number of cubes in a layer by the number of layers, the volume of the solid is found. This is the unifying idea that volume for a solid is found by finding the area of the base (B) and multiplying by the average height (h) or number of layers in the solid. The difficulty lies in finding the area of the triangular or circular base (B).

Materials
Triangular Prism and Cylinder (prior investigation)
Centimeter cubes, 10 per group (Item #1920)
Tape
Metric ruler

HAVE EACH GROUP USE THE PRISM AND CYLINDER THEY MADE IN SPECIAL BOX BUILDING.

EACH GROUP MAKES A LAYER BY TAPING CENTICUBES TO A "LAYER" SILHOUETTE FROM THE ORIGINAL TEMPLATE PAGE. THEY PUT THIS FIRST LAYER IN THE BOX.

THE GROUP USES THEIR REMAINING CUBES TO SEE HOW MANY LAYERS WOULD STACK UP TO FILL THE BOX.

EACH GROUP CALCULATES THE AREA OF A LAYER.

EMPHASIZE THE MEANING OF THE EQUATION. FINDING THE AREA OF THE BASE TELLS THE NUMBER OF CUBES IN A LAYER. MULTIPLYING A LAYER (BASE) BY THE HEIGHT (THE NUMBER OF LAYERS) TELLS THE VOLUME.

GATHER ALL THE GROUPS' LAYERS AND FILL THE CLASS DEMONSTRATION BOX TO CONFIRM UNDERSTANDING.

FILLING SPECIAL BOXES

HOW MANY CENTIMETER CUBES WILL IT TAKE TO FILL YOUR *TRIANGULAR PRISM* AND *CYLINDER*?

(B • h) ÷ 2 IS THE FORMULA FOR THE TRIANGULAR BASE

THE *HEIGHT* OF THE PRISM TELLS HOW MANY LAYERS FIT IN THE PRISM.

Triangular Base
base: **12** cm
height: **6** cm
area: **36** cm^2

Layers in prism — height: **5** cm
Volume of prism — volume: **180** cm^3

πr^2 IS THE FORMULA FOR THE CIRCULAR BASE.

THE *HEIGHT* OF THE CYLINDER TELLS HOW MANY LAYERS FIT IN THE CYLINDER.

Circular Base
radius: **3.5** cm
radius square: **12.25** cm^2
area: **38.47** cm^2

Layers in cylinder — height: **6** cm
Volume of cylinder — volume: **230.82** cm^3

How do you find how many cubes are in a layer of a prism or a cylinder?
Find the area of the base.
How do you determine the number of layers in a box?
Measure the height of the box.
How can you use the number of cubes in a layer and the number of layers in a box to determine the number of cubes in a box?
Multiply cubes in a layer by the number of layers.

PRISMS, PYRAMIDS, CYLINDE...

Animation

Seeing a prism and cylinder filled a layer at a time provides a visual model of the formulas or procedures for finding the volume.

Reinforces the use of the formula V = B · h for finding the volume of prisms and cylinders.

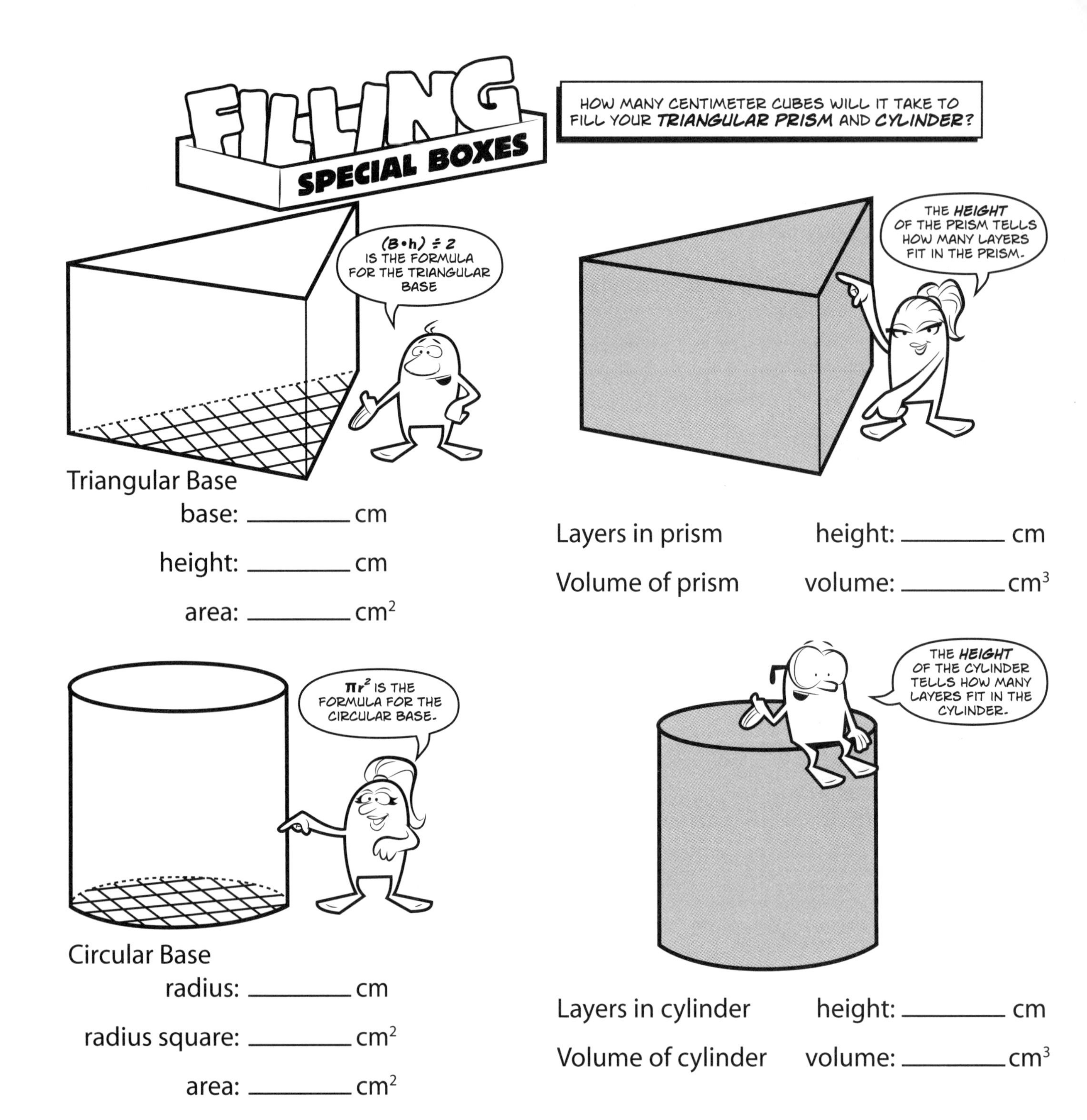

How do you find how many cubes are in a layer of a prism or a cylinder?

How do you determine the number of layers in a box?

How can you use the number of cubes in a layer and the number of layers in a box to determine the number of cubes in a box?

Animation

How does the formula for the volume of a prism or cylinder describe what fills the prism or cylinder?

What is the formulas for finding the area of each of the three shapes?

What is the area of each of the shapes?

The shapes from the frame above form the bases of the solids and are covered with cubes or parts of cubes. Each of these layers are one cube thick.

What is the volume of each of the three layers?

How many layers are in each of these solids?

How do you determine the volume, or number of little cubes, in each of these solids?

Write a formula that calculates the volume of each of the solids and explain how each formula relates to what is seen in the animation.

MEASUREMENT OF PRISMS, PYRAMIDS, CYLINDERS, AND CONES
ESSENTIAL MATH SERIES
Filling Special Boxes
THINGS TO LOOK FOR:
1. WHY CAN'T YOU MEASURE THE VOLUME OF THE TRIANGULAR-BASED PRISM AND CYLINDER THE SAME WAY THAT YOU DID THE VOLUME OF THE SQUARED-BASED PRISM BY FILLING IT WITH CUBES?
2. WHY DOES THE FORMULA V = B • h WORK FOR BOTH THE TRIANGULAR-BASED PRISM AND THE CYLINDER? WILL THIS FORMULA WORK FOR ANY CYLINDER OR PRISM?
IN THE PREVIOUS ACTIVITY WE FOUND THE SURFACE AREA OF THESE TWO SOLIDS, A TRIANGULAR PRISM AND A CYLINDER.
IN THIS ACTIVITY WE FOUND THE VOLUMES OF THESE TWO SOLIDS.
TOP
TOP
YEAH, IT WAS A LOT LIKE WHAT WE DID TO FIND THE VOLUME OF THE PRISM WITH A SQUARE BASE.
LIKE, FOR THE PRISM WITH THE SQUARE BASE, WE FIRST HAD TO FIGURE OUT HOW MANY CUBES WOULD BE IN A LAYER.
THE CUBES EXACTLY FIT ON TOP OF THE SQUARES THAT COVERED THE BASE. THAT'S HOW WE KNEW THAT THE NUMBER OF CUBES IN A LAYER WAS THE SAME AS THE AREA OF THE BASE.
THEN WE STACKED UP THE LAYERS UNTIL THE BOX WAS FULL.
WE FOUND OUT THAT THE HEIGHT WAS THE SAME AS THE NUMBER OF LAYERS IT TOOK TO FILL THE BOX.
THAT MEANS THAT VOLUME IS THE AREA OF THE BASE TIMES THE HEIGHT.
SO, WE FOUND THE VOLUME OF THE TRIANGULAR PRISM AND THE CYLINDER THE SAME WAY!
TRUE.
WE JUST MULTIPLIED THE AREA OF THE BASES TIMES THE HEIGHTS.
BUT YOU CAN'T PUT THE RIGHT NUMBER OF CUBES IN A LAYER WHEN THE BASE IS A TRIANGLE OR A CIRCLE.
LIKE, YOU CAN ONLY GET 21 CUBES IN A LAYER FOR THE TRIANGULAR PRISM, BUT THE AREA OF THE BASE IS 24 1/2.
1
WELL, YEAH, RED, THAT'S TRUE.
TO COMPLETELY FILL IT YOU'D HAVE TO CUT SOME CUBES IN HALF TO FILL IN THE EMPTY SPACES.
THAT'S RIGHT, MARK. HERE'S A PICUTRE OF WHAT IT WOULD LOOK LIKE IF YOU DID CUT SOME OF THEM IN HALF AND FIT THEM INTO THOSE EMPTY SPACES.
YOU CAN SEE IN THIS PICTURE THAT THE CUBES EXACTLY FIT ON TOP OF THE SQUARES THAT SHOW THE AREA OF THE BASE. THAT'S HOW WE KNOW THAT THE NUMBER OF CUBES IN A LAYER IS THE SAME AS THE AREA OF THE BASE.
FOR THE CIRCLE, IT WOULD TAKE A LOT OF WORK TO ROUND OFF PARTS OF SOME OF THE CUBES IN ORDER TO FIT THEM IN THE EMPTY SPACES.
BUT, IF WE COULD MAKE THAT LAYER OF CUBES, HERE'S WHAT IT WOULD LOOK LIKE, AND YOU CAN SEE THAT THE CUBES EXACTLY FIT ON TOP OF THE SQUARES ON THE BASE.
SO, CLASS, FOR ANY PRISM OR CYLINDER, THE AREA OF THE BASE WILL ALWAYS TELL YOU HOW MANY CUBES ARE IN A LAYER.
AND THE HEIGHT TELLS US HOW MANY LAYERS ARE IN THE SOLIDS!
EXACTLY. OKAY, CLASS, WHAT WAS THE VOLUME OF THE TRIANGULAR PRISM?
THE AREA OF THE BASE WAS 24 1/2 AND WE FOUND THAT THE HEIGHT WAS 6.
THAT'S 147 CUBIC CENTIMETERS.
24 1/2
height 6
OKAY, WHAT ABOUT THE CYLINDER? WHAT WAS ITS VOLUME?
AAH, THAT WAS A TOUGH ONE. I'M NOT SURE I UNDERSTAND HOW TO FIND IT.
2

WELL, WE DID IT THE SAME WAY. THE BASE OF THE CYLINDER WAS A CIRCLE WITH A DIAMETER OF 7.
SO, THEN, THE RADIUS WAS 3 1/2, AND THE HEIGHT WAS 6. WE JUST NEEDED TO USE THE FORMULA FOR THE AREA OF A CIRCLE, A = π · r², TO FIND THE AREA OF THE BASE. THEN WE MULTIPLIED THAT TIMES THE HEIGHT TO GET THE VOLUME. IT WAS 231 CUBIC CENTIMETERS.
r = 3 1/2 = 3.5
A = 3.14 · 12.25 = 38.47 or 38.5
height 6
V = 38.5 · 6 = 231
DOES THAT WORK FOR EVERY PRISM OR CYLINDER?
DO WE JUST HAVE TO FIND THE AREA OF THE BASE AND THE HEIGHT AND THEN MULTIPLY THEM?
YES! IT DOES WORK FOR EVERY PRISM AND CYLINDER, REDMOND.
WHOA. DID YOU FEEL THAT? I THINK MY MIND GOT ROCKED.
THAT FORMULA, V = B · h, THAT YOU GAVE FOR THE SQUARE-BASED PRISM WORKS FOR ALL OF THESE SOLIDS, RIGHT?
THAT'S RIGHT. THIS FORMULA WORKS FOR EVERY PRISM OR CYLINDER.
WHY IS THERE A CAPITAL B IN THE FORMULA? DON'T WE USUALLY USE THE CAPITAL LETTER A FOR THE AREA OF SOMETHING?
USUALLY WE DO USE THE CAPITAL LETTER A FOR AREA. HOWEVER, IN THIS FORMULA, WE USED THE CAPITAL LETTER B BECAUSE WE WANT TO EMPHASIZE AND REMEMBER THAT THIS IS THE AREA OF THE BASE OF THE CYLINDER.
B = 7 · 7 = 49
7
7
B = 1/2 · 7 · 7 = 24 1/2
7
7
r = 3 1/2 = 3.5
B = 3.14 · 12.25 = 38.47 or 38.5
WHAT IF I GAVE YOU THIS PRISM WITH A PENTAGON BASE. WHAT IS THE VOLUME?
B = 28 sq cm
h = 9 cm
WELL, YOU WROTE THERE THAT THE AREA OF THE BASE IS 28, SO WE DON'T HAVE TO FIGURE THAT OUT.
THAT MEANS THAT B IS 28 AND AND h IS 9. SO, WE JUST MULTIPLY 28 TIMES 9. THE VOLUME IS 252 CUBIC CENTIMETERS.
V = B · h
= 28 · 9
= 252 cubic cm
CLASS, I THINK YOU'RE READY FOR THE NEXT TWO ACTIVITIES, WHERE WE'LL BE USING THESE IDEAS.
3

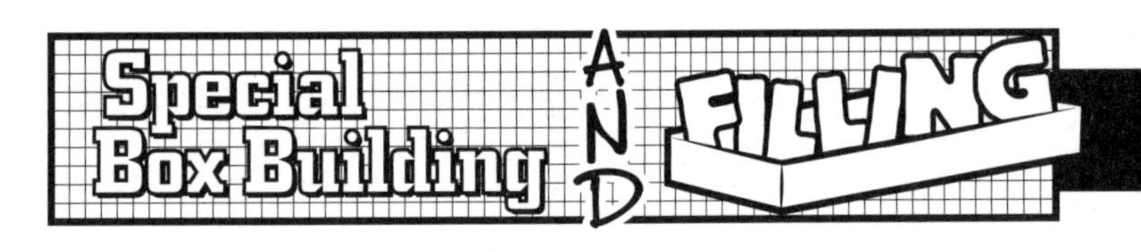

Practice

Students apply their learning to more abstract situations.

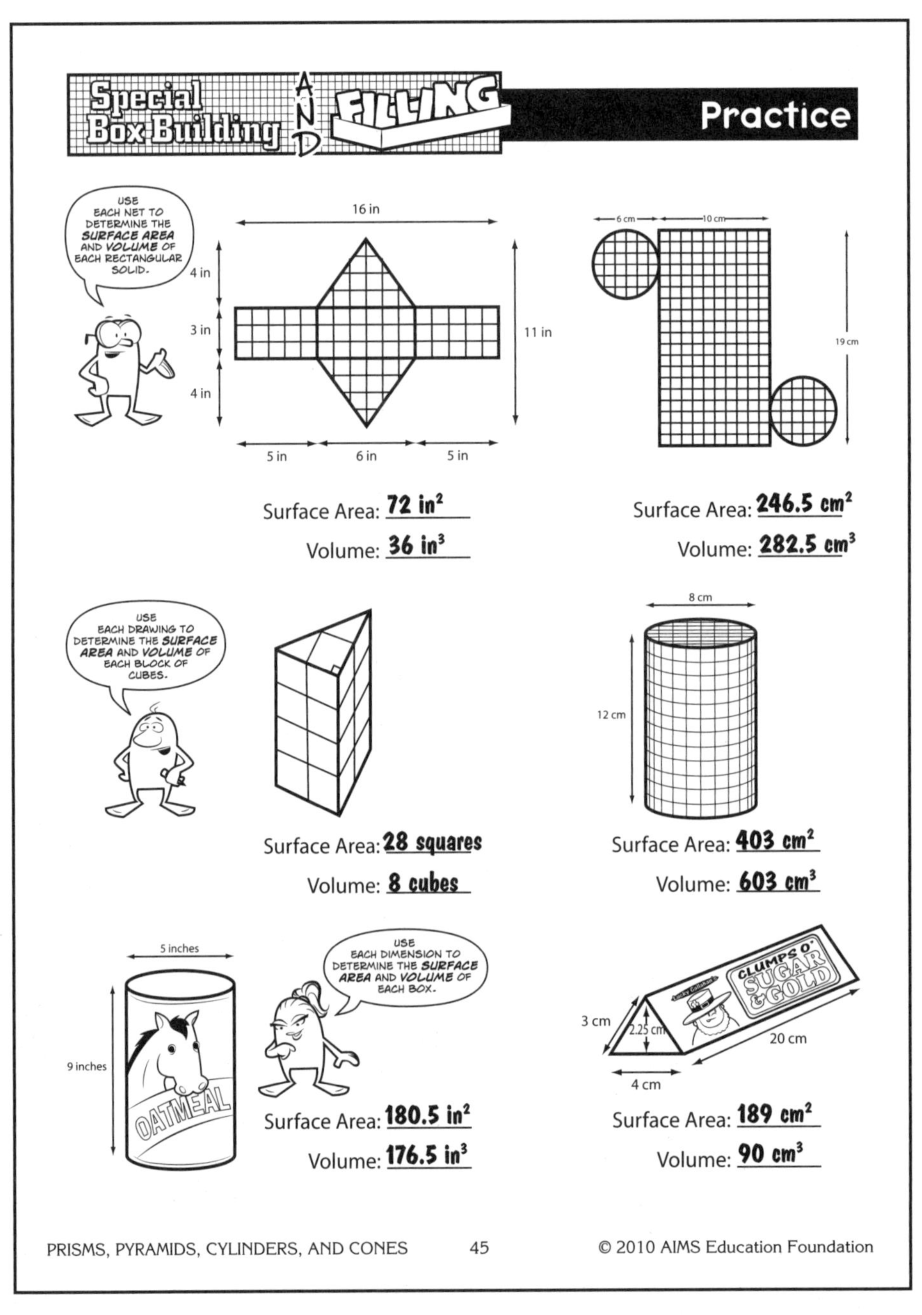
Special Box Building AND FILLING

Practice

USE EACH NET TO DETERMINE THE SURFACE AREA AND VOLUME OF EACH RECTANGULAR SOLID.

16 in; 4 in; 3 in; 4 in; 11 in; 5 in; 6 in; 5 in

Surface Area: 72 in²

Volume: 36 in³

6 cm; 10 cm; 19 cm

Surface Area: 246.5 cm²

Volume: 282.5 cm³

USE EACH DRAWING TO DETERMINE THE SURFACE AREA AND VOLUME OF EACH BLOCK OF CUBES.

Surface Area: 28 squares

Volume: 8 cubes

8 cm; 12 cm

Surface Area: 403 cm²

Volume: 603 cm³

USE EACH DIMENSION TO DETERMINE THE SURFACE AREA AND VOLUME OF EACH BOX.

5 inches; 9 inches; OATMEAL

Surface Area: 180.5 in²

Volume: 176.5 in³

CLUMPS O' SUGAR & GOLD

3 cm; 2.25 cm; 4 cm; 20 cm

Surface Area: 189 cm²

Volume: 90 cm³

PRISMS, PYRAMIDS, CYLINDERS, AND CONES 45 © 2010 AIMS Education Foundation

Special Box Building AND FILLING

Practice

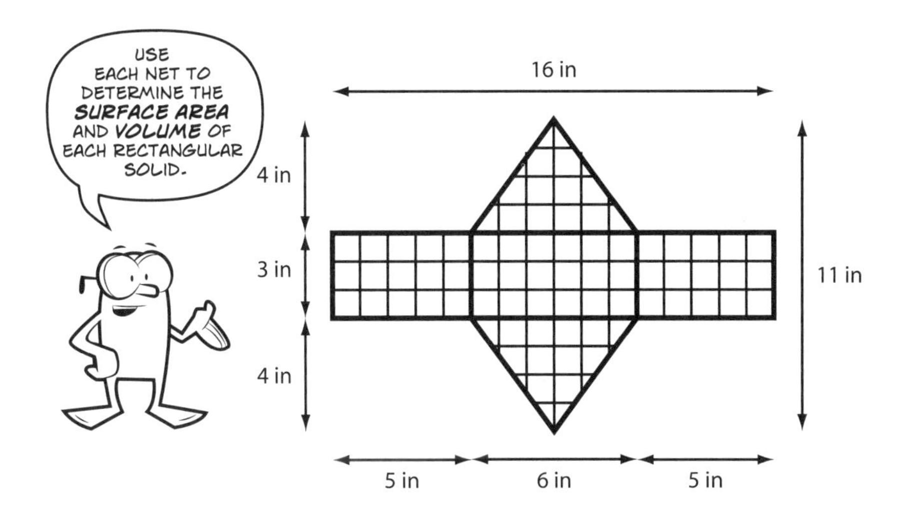

Surface Area: ________

Volume: ________

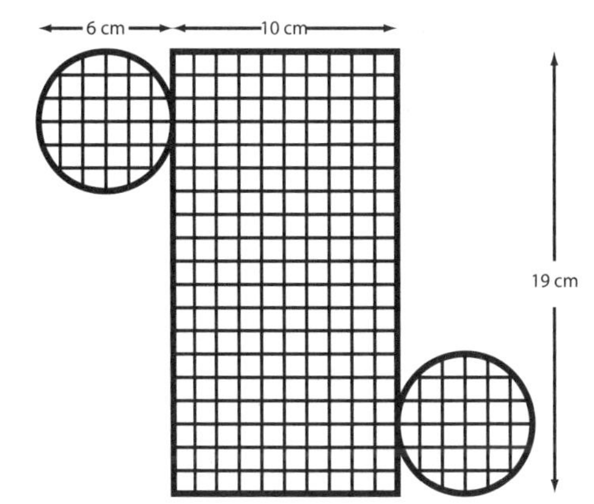

Surface Area: ________

Volume: ________

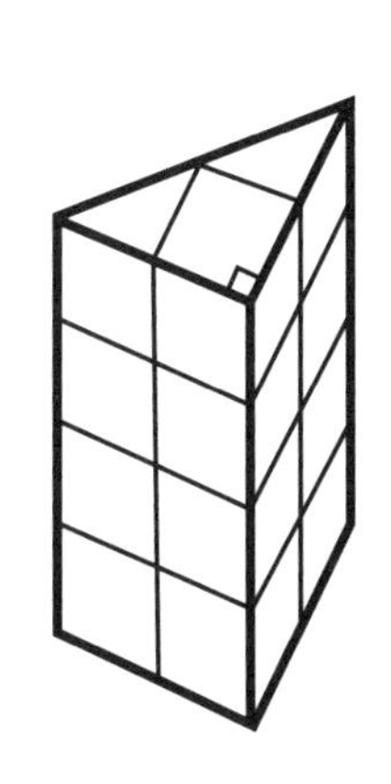

Surface Area: ________

Volume: ________

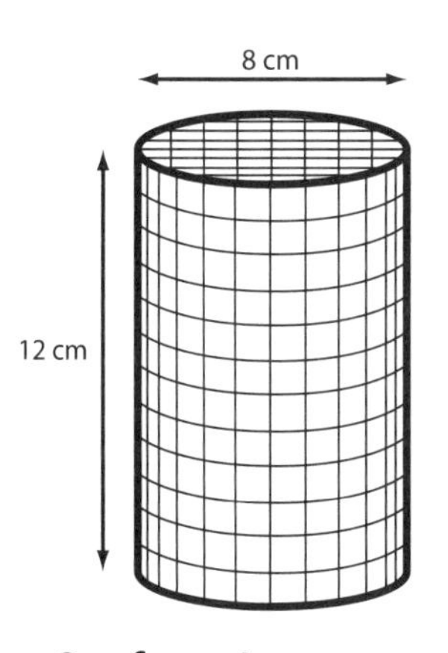

Surface Area: ________

Volume: ________

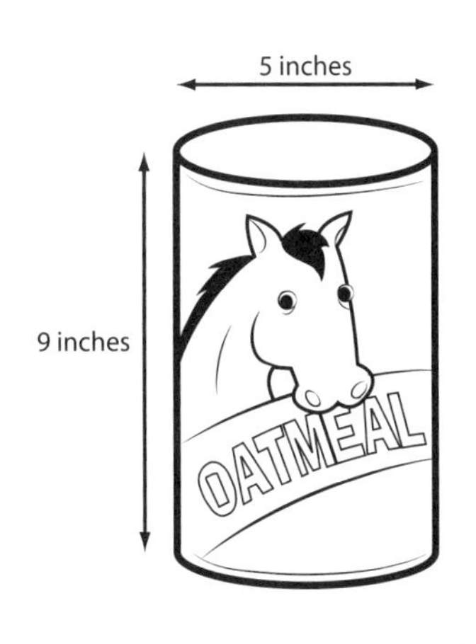

Surface Area: ________

Volume: ________

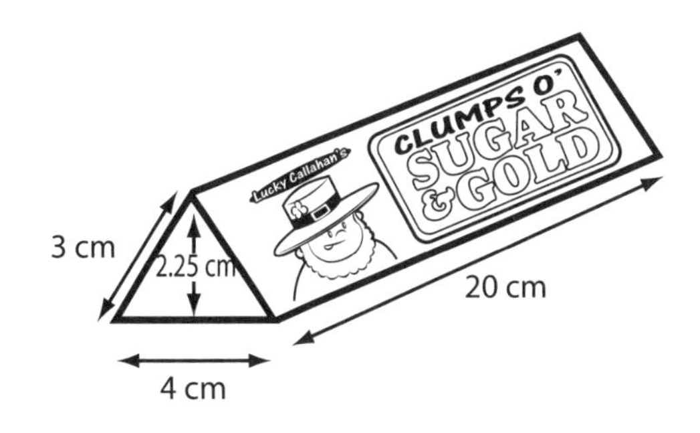

Surface Area: ________

Volume: ________

Building Pointed Boxes

How do you determine how much cardboard it takes to build a box in the shape of rectangular-based pyramid, a triangular-based pyramid, or a cone?

Building a box from a net is an opportunity to identify the shapes used to make all the surfaces of the solid. Seeing the net reinforces the idea of surface area as a measure of covering and a sum of the areas of all the shapes on the surfaces surrounding the solid.

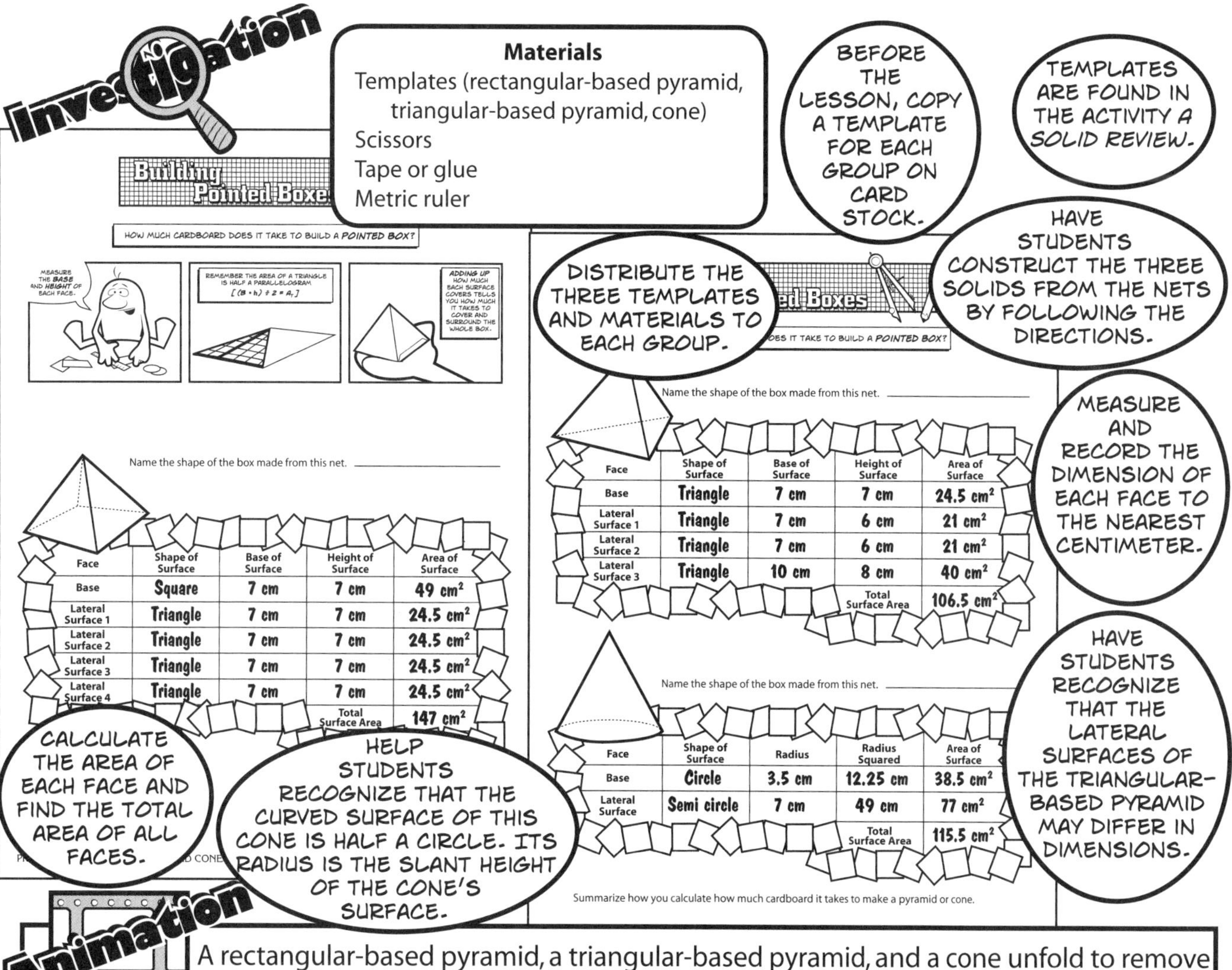

Face	Shape of Surface	Base of Surface	Height of Surface	Area of Surface
Base	Square	7 cm	7 cm	49 cm²
Lateral Surface 1	Triangle	7 cm	7 cm	24.5 cm²
Lateral Surface 2	Triangle	7 cm	7 cm	24.5 cm²
Lateral Surface 3	Triangle	7 cm	7 cm	24.5 cm²
Lateral Surface 4	Triangle	7 cm	7 cm	24.5 cm²
			Total Surface Area	147 cm²

Face	Shape of Surface	Base of Surface	Height of Surface	Area of Surface
Base	Triangle	7 cm	7 cm	24.5 cm²
Lateral Surface 1	Triangle	7 cm	6 cm	21 cm²
Lateral Surface 2	Triangle	7 cm	6 cm	21 cm²
Lateral Surface 3	Triangle	10 cm	8 cm	40 cm²
			Total Surface Area	106.5 cm²

Face	Shape of Surface	Radius	Radius Squared	Area of Surface
Base	Circle	3.5 cm	12.25 cm	38.5 cm²
Lateral Surface	Semi circle	7 cm	49 cm	77 cm²
			Total Surface Area	115.5 cm²

Animation

A rectangular-based pyramid, a triangular-based pyramid, and a cone unfold to remove their skins leaving the nets and interiors. The concept of surface area is illustrated.

Comics

Part 1: Compares finding the surface areas of a square-based pyramid and a triangular-based pyramid.

Part 2: Looks at the process of finding the surace area of a cone.

Demonstrates with physical models how to determine the surface area by determining the type, size, and number of the polygons and shapes that compose the surface.

HOW MUCH CARDBOARD DOES IT TAKE TO BUILD A ***POINTED BOX***?

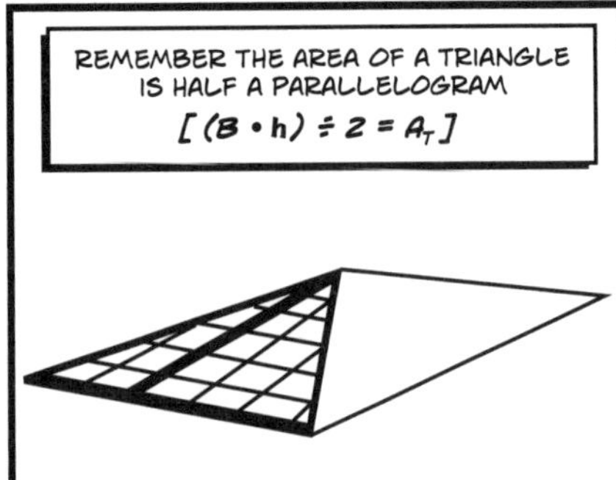

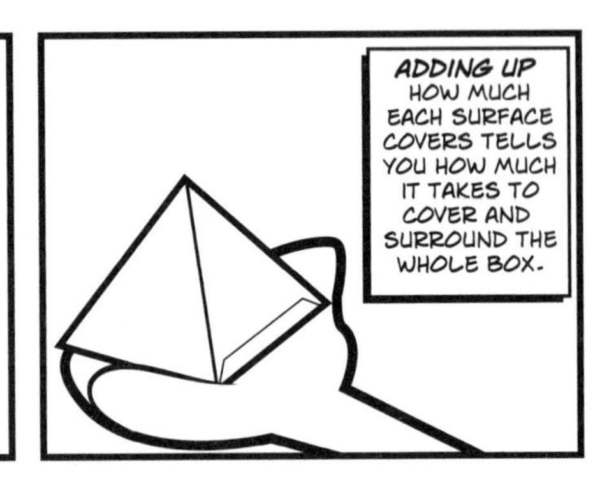

Name the shape of the box made from this net. ____________________

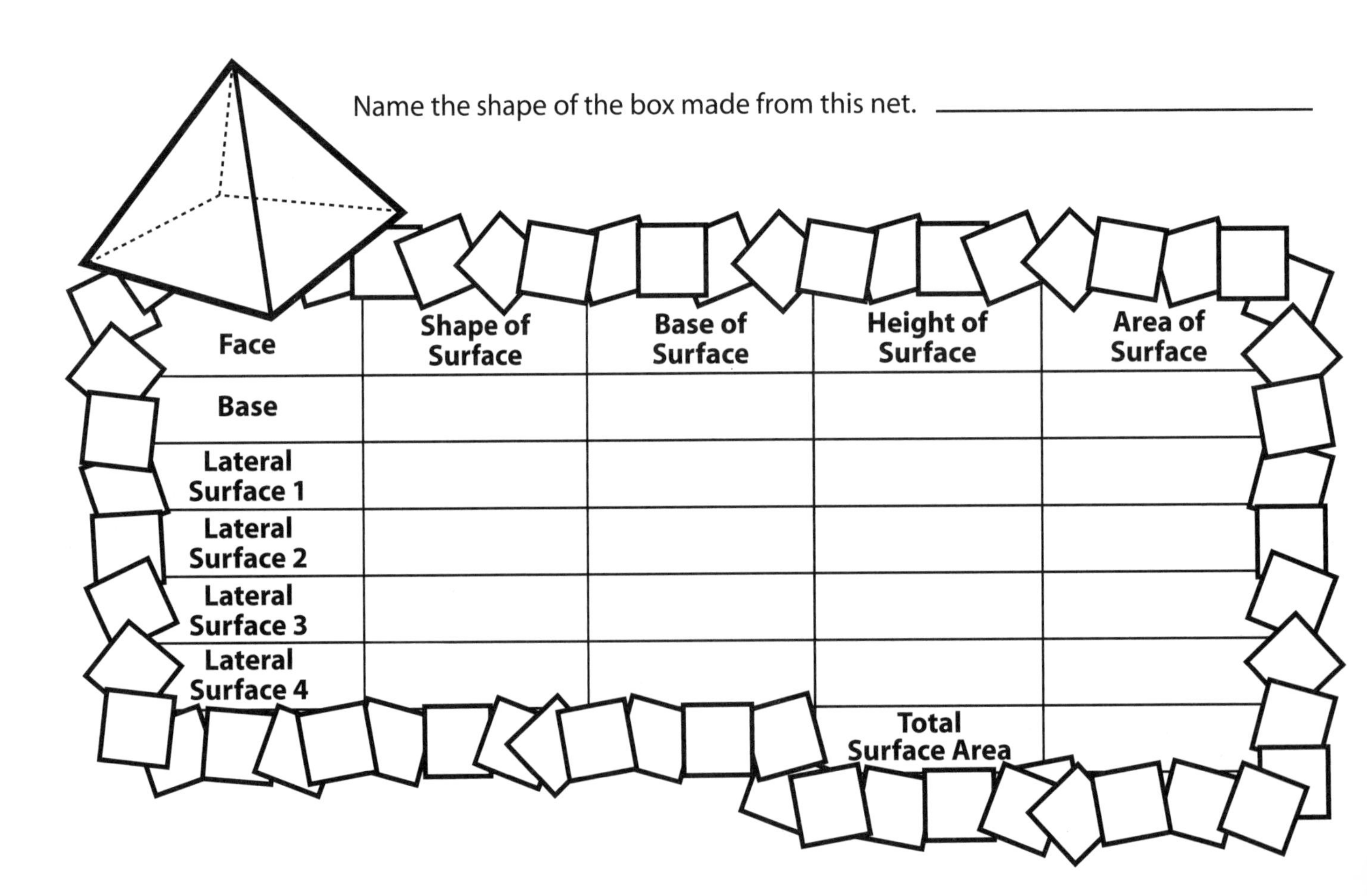

Face	Shape of Surface	Base of Surface	Height of Surface	Area of Surface
Base				
Lateral Surface 1				
Lateral Surface 2				
Lateral Surface 3				
Lateral Surface 4				
			Total Surface Area	

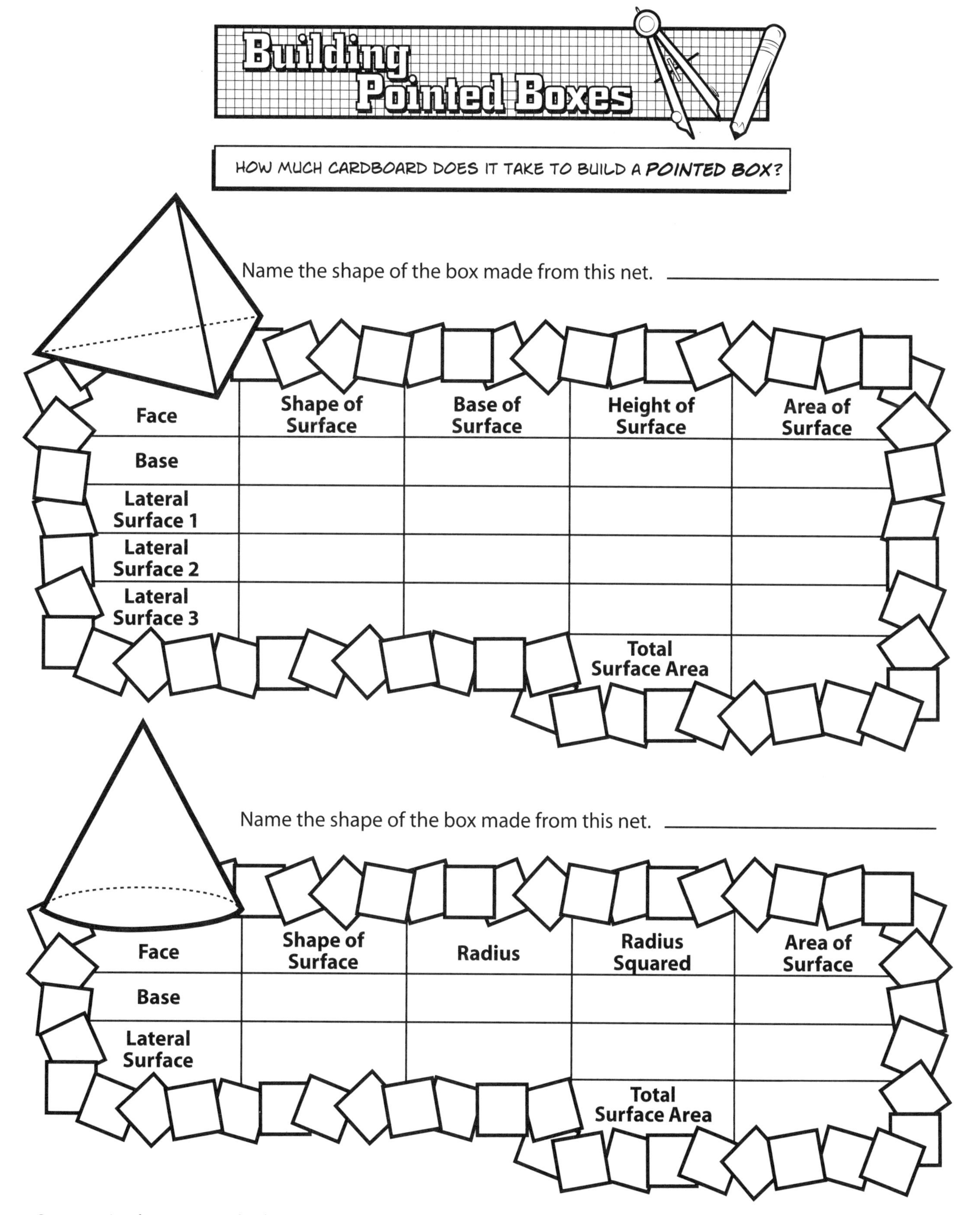

Building Pointed Boxes

HOW MUCH CARDBOARD DOES IT TAKE TO BUILD A ***POINTED BOX***?

Name the shape of the box made from this net. ____________________

Face	Shape of Surface	Base of Surface	Height of Surface	Area of Surface
Base				
Lateral Surface 1				
Lateral Surface 2				
Lateral Surface 3				
			Total Surface Area	

Name the shape of the box made from this net. ____________________

Face	Shape of Surface	Radius	Radius Squared	Area of Surface
Base				
Lateral Surface				
			Total Surface Area	

Summarize how you calculate how much cardboard it takes to make a pyramid or cone.

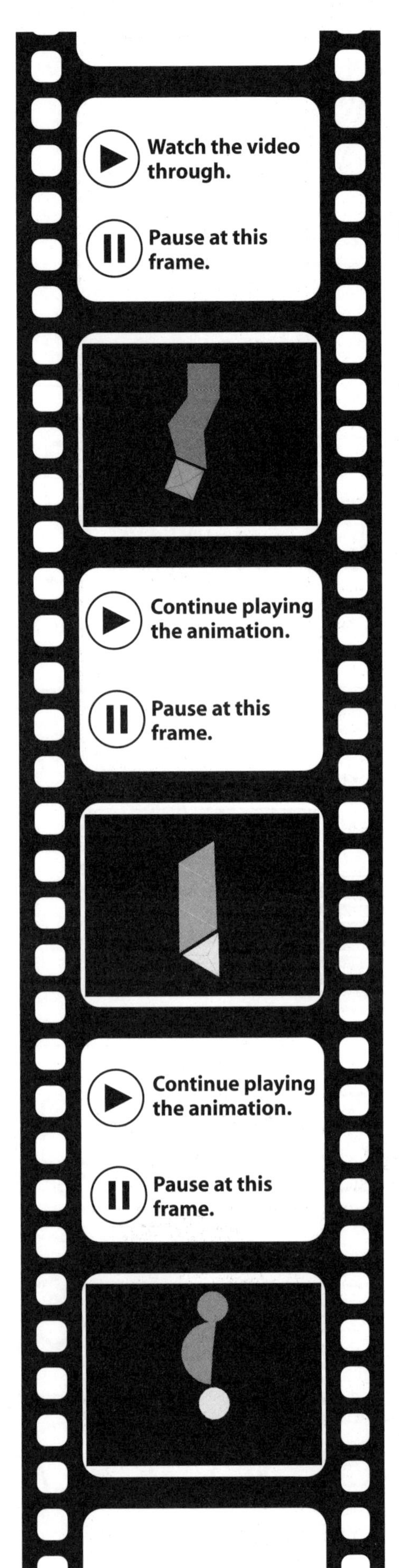

Unfolding Pointed Boxes

How do you find the surface area of pyramids and cones?

Identify the shapes needed to make this solid by outlining each face or surface on the net.

How can you use the shapes you identified to find the surface area of this pyramid?

Identify the shapes needed to make this solid by outlining each face or surface on the net.

How can you use the shapes you identified to find the surface area of this pyramid?

Identify the shapes needed to make this solid by outlining each face or surface on the net.

How can you use the shapes you identified to find the surface area of this cone?

Summarize how you find the surface area of a pyramid or cone.

MEASUREMENT OF PRISMS, PYRAMIDS, CYLINDERS, AND CONES
ESSENTIAL MATH SERIES
Building Pointed Boxes, Part 1
THINGS TO LOOK FOR:
1. WHAT IS THE NAME OF THE VERTEX THAT IS THE TOP POINT OF A PYRAMID?
2. WHAT SHAPE FORMS THE LATERAL FACES OF A PYRAMID?
3. WHY CAN YOU USE THE LENGTH OF ONE OF THE SIDES AS THE HEIGHT FOR TRIANGLES A AND B, BUT YOU CAN'T DO THAT FOR TRIANGLE C?
IN THIS ACTIVITY, WE BUILT A CONE AND TWO PYRAMIDS.
WE CALLED THEM POINTED BOXES.
YES, THAT'S BECAUSE THEY ALL HAVE A POINT ON TOP.
MS. CHO, IS THERE A SPECIAL NAME FOR THAT POINT ON TOP?
SHOULDN'T WE CALL IT A VERTEX? THAT'S WHAT WE CALL THE POINT WHERE EDGES OR SIDES COME TOGETHER, LIKE AT THE CORNER OF A TRIANGLE.
IT'S REALLY CALLED THE APEX. WE DON'T USE THAT WORD VERY OFTEN, AND IF YOU CALL IT A VERTEX OR YOU JUST CALL IT THE TOP POINT, THAT WILL BE OKAY.
LET'S TALK ABOUT EACH OF THESE THREE SHAPES, STARTING WITH THE PYRAMID WITH A SQUARE BASE.
YOU STARTED WITH THIS NET, RIGHT?
TAB
WHAT DO YOU KNOW ABOUT THE FOUR TRIANGULAR FACES OF THIS PYRAMID?
THEY ARE CONGRUENT. THEY'RE THE SAME SIZE AND SHAPE.
AND THEY'RE CALLED LATERAL FACES. THAT'S BECAUSE THEY FIT AROUND THE SIDES OF THE BASE, AND THEY ALL COME TOGETHER AT THE APEX.
AND DON'T FORGET THAT THEY ARE ISOSCELES TRIANGLES BECAUSE EACH OF THEM HAS TWO EQUAL SIDES.
1
OKAY, SO HERE IS A PICTURE OF THE NET AND TWO DIFFERENT VIEWS OF THE PYRAMID THAT IT MAKES.
BASE
TAB
BASE
WHAT DID YOU DO TO FIND THE SURFACE AREA OF THIS PYRAMID?
WE JUST HAD TO FIND THE AREA OF EACH OF THE LATERAL FACES AND THE BASE, AND THEN ADD THEM UP.
THE BASE IS A SQUARE THAT'S 7 BY 7 CENTIMETERS. THE AREA IS 49 SQUARE CENTIMETERS, THE SAME AS THE SQUARE-BASED PRISM.
BASE
7 cm
7 cm
THE FOUR LATERAL FACES ARE CONGRUENT TRIANGLES, SO WE JUST HAD TO FIND THE AREA OF ONE OF THEM AND MULTIPLY BY 4.
I MEASURED THE HEIGHT OF ONE FACE, AND IT WAS 7 CENTIMETERS, THE SAME AS THE LENGTH OF THE BASE. THEN WE USED THE FORMULA FOR THE AREA OF THE TRIANGLE.
A = 1/2 · 7 · 7 = 24 1/2
7 cm
7 cm
THE TOTAL AREA OF THE FOUR TRIANGLES WAS 4 TIMES 24 1/2, WHICH WAS 98. WHEN WE ADDED IN THE AREA OF THE BASE, 49, WE GOT 147 SQUARE CENTIMETERS AS THE SURFACE OF THE PYRAMID.
4 · (24 1/2) = 98
4 triangles 98
square base 49
surface area of pyramid 147 sq. cm
THIS PYRAMID WAS EASIER THAN THE ONE WITH A TRIANGLE BASE.
NO IT WASN'T, RED. WE DID IT THE SAME WAY FOR BOTH.
BUT THE TRIANGLES WEREN'T ALL THE SAME!
OKAY, REDMOND, LET'S TALK ABOUT THE TRIANGULAR- BASED PYRAMID.
YOU'RE RIGHT, THE TRIANGLES AREN'T ALL THE SAME. IN FACT, ONLY TWO OF THEM ARE CONGRUENT.
THE TWO TRIANGLES A AND B ARE CONGRUENT AND SHARE THE SIDE LENGTH 6.
TRIANGLE C AND THE BASE ARE DIFFERENT FROM A AND B AND FROM EACH OTHER.
A
B
C
BASE
7
7
6
7
10
HERE ARE TWO VIEWS OF THE PYRAMID THAT YOU MADE FROM THIS NET.
WHAT ARE THE AREAS OF THE DIFFERENT FACES?
10
7
7
6
6
10
7
2

THREE OF THE FACES HAVE RIGHT ANGLES, RIGHT?
YES, THEY DO. WHAT'S HELPFUL ABOUT KNOWING THEY WERE RIGHT TRIANGLES?
BECAUSE THAT MEANT THAT TWO SIDES OF EACH OF THE TRIANGLES WERE THE BASE AND THE HEIGHT.
SO, THE AREA OF THE BASE TRIANGLE IS 1/2 · 7 · 7 = 24 1/2.
BASE
7
7
AND, THE AREA OF THE BASE TRIANGLE IS 1/2 · 6 · 7 = 21.
7
A
6
BUT WHAT ABOUT TRIANGLE C? I KNOW THE BASE WAS 10, BUT WHAT ABOUT THE HEIGHT?
GOOD QUESTION CLASS, HOW CAN YOU FIND THE HEIGHT FOR THIS TRIANGLE?
YOU JUST MEASURE UP FROM THE BASE TO THE THE POINT AT THE TOP.
10
WHAT I FOUND OUT WAS THAT THE HEIGHT WASN'T QUITE 8.
INSTEAD, I GOT 7 3/4.
6
7
10
THAT'S RIGHT, SHUTTLE, IT'S ALMOST EXACTLY 7 3/4. BY THE WAY, IF YOU CHANGE THE FRACTIONS TO DECIMALS, YOU CAN USE YOUR CALCULATORS.
7.75
8
7
10
ONCE I KNEW THE HEIGHT, I FOUND THE AREA OF THE TRIANGLE USING THE FORMULA, SAME AS THE OTHERS.
WHEN I ADDED UP THE AREAS OF THE FOUR FACES, I FOUND THAT THE SURFACE AREA WAS 105.25 SQUARE CENTIMETERS.
38.75
24.5
21
21
105.25 sq. cm
.5 · 10 · 7.75 = 38.75
7.75
6
10
7
.5 · 7 · 7 = 24.5
10
7
7
6
.5 · 7 · 6 = 21
.5 · 7 · 6 = 21
3

MEASUREMENT OF PRISMS, PYRAMIDS, CYLINDERS, AND CONES
ESSENTIAL MATH SERIES
Building Pointed Boxes, Part 2
THINGS TO LOOK FOR:
1. HOW IS A CONE LIKE A PYRAMID?
2. WHY DOES A CONE HAVE ONLY ONE VERTEX? (BY THE WAY, THAT ONE VERTEX IS CALLED THE APEX.)
THE LAST SHAPE WE BUILT WAS A CONE. THE NET LOOKED LIKE THIS.
TAB
BASE
THAT WAS PRETTY COOL. I DIDN'T KNOW THAT THE CURVED PART OF A CONE IS FORMED BY HALF OF A CIRCLE.
WELL, ELORA, YOU'RE RIGHT, THIS ONE WAS MADE FROM HALF OF A CIRCLE.
BASE
BUT, CLASS, I WANT YOU TO KNOW THAT THERE ARE CONES WHERE THIS CURVED SURFACE IS MORE THAN HALF OF A CIRCLE, AND OTHERS WHERE IT IS LESS THAN HALF OF A CIRCLE.
TAB
TAB
HERE YOU SEE OUR CONE IN THE MIDDLE, AND TWO OTHERS. NOTICE THAT WHEN THE NET IS MORE THAN A HALF CIRCLE, THE BASE IS BIGGER AND THE CONE IS SHORTER AND FLATTER. WHEN THE NET IS LESS THAN A HALF CIRCLE THE BASE IS SMALLER, BUT THE CONE IS TALLER AND STEEPER.
LET'S GET BACK TO OUR CONE.
WE'LL START BY TALKING ABOUT HOW YOU FOUND THE AREA OF THE CURVED SURFACE.
MS. CHO, I MEASURED THE LINE FROM THE BASE TO THE TOP POINT. IT WAS 7 CENTIMETERS.
BUT, THEN I DIDN'T KNOW WHAT TO MULTIPLY IT BY.
7 cm
1
I DID THAT TOO, BUT THEN I LOOKED BACK AT THE NET.
THE RADIUS OF THE CIRCLE IS 7. THE AREA OF THE CURVED SURFACE IS THE SAME AS THE AREA OF THE HALF CIRCLE.
r = 7
TAB
THE AREA OF A WHOLE CIRCLE IS PI TIMES THE RADIUS SQUARED, SO THE AREA OF THE HALF CIRCLE IS HALF OF THAT.
$A = \pi^2 \cdot r$
area of a whole circle
$3.14 \cdot 7^2 = 153.86$ sq. cm
area of a half circle
= 76.93 sq. cm
WELL DONE, SHUTTLE. ELORA, DO YOU SEE THAT THE LINE THAT YOU MEASURED ON THE CONE WAS THE SAME AS THE RADIUS OF THE HALF CIRCLE?
I SEE THAT NOW!
NOW YOU KNOW THE AREA OF THE CURVED SURFACE, HOW ABOUT THE AREA OF THE BASE?
THAT WAS EASY. WE JUST USED THE FORMULA FOR THE AREA OF A CIRCLE, PI TIMES THE RADIUS SQUARED.
WE KNEW THE DIAMETER OF THE BASE WAS 7, SO THE RADIUS WAS HALF THAT, OR 3.5
r = 3.5
d = 7
WHEN WE USED THE FORMULA, WE FOUND THAT THE AREA WAS 38.47 SQUARE CENTIMETERS.
$A = \pi \cdot (3.5)^2$
$= 3.14 \cdot (12.25)$
= 3847 sq. cm
ACTUALLY, MARK, YOU DIDN'T HAVE TO DO ALL THAT WORK. THIS BASE WAS THE SAME AS THE BASE OF THE CYLINDER WE DID EARLIER.
WE ALREADY FOUND THE AREA WHEN WE DID THE CYLINDER. WE ROUNDED IT OFF TO 38.5.
YEAH... YEAH, I KNEW THAT.
OKAY, CLASS, LET'S FINISH UP WITH THE CONE.
r = 3.5
d = 7
3847 sq. cm
76.93 sq. cm
r = 7
surface area of the cone
115.4 sq. cm
MS. CHO, THE DIAMETER OF THE BASE OF THE CONE AND THE RADIUS OF THE HALF CIRCLE WERE BOTH 7. ARE THOSE TWO MEASUREMENTS ALWAYS THE SAME?
THEY WILL BE THE SAME WHENEVER THE CURVED SURFACE IS FORMED BY HALF A CIRCLE. OTHERWISE, THOSE MEASUREMENTS WILL BE DIFFERENT.
CLASS, YOU'VE LEARNED A LOT ABOUT PYRAMIDS AND CONES, BUT THERE'S STILL MORE TO KNOW!
2

How do you determine how many centimeter cubes it takes to fill pyramid or cone?

By transferring cereal from a pyramid or cone to a prism or cylinder with equal bases (B) and heights (h), one discovers that a pyramid or cone is one-third the volume of a prism or cylinder with the same dimensions.

Investigation

Materials

All 6 solids from prior investigations *(rectangular solid, triangular prism, cylinder, square-based pyramid, triangular-based pyramid, cone)*
Box of crisped rice cereal
Paper cups
Metric ruler
100 mL graduated cylinder, optional (Item #1927)

HAVE EACH GROUP GATHER THE SOLIDS THEY MADE IN THE EARLIER INVESTIGATIONS.

HAVE STUDENTS LOOK AT THE RECORD. EMPHASIZE HOW EACH POINTED BOX FILLS ONE-THIRD OF ITS PAIRED SOLID.

AS STUDENTS PAIR UP THE PRISM OR CYLINDER WITH THE CORRESPONDING PYRAMID OR CONE THEY SHOULD RECOGNIZE THAT THEY HAVE THE SAME BASES AND HEIGHTS.

MEASUREMENTS CAN BE TAKEN FROM PRIOR INVESTIGATIONS OR RECALCULATED.

EACH GROUP NEEDS A CUP OF CEREAL.

POURING THE CEREAL FROM A PYRAMID OR CONE INTO A GRADUATED CYLINDER CONFIRMS THE SOLUTION.

FILL EACH POINTED BOX AND POUR IT INTO ITS PAIRED SOLID.

PAIR THE PYRAMIDS AND CONE WITH THEIR CORRESPONDING PRISM OR CYLINDER.

FILL EACH PYRAMID AND CONE WITH CRISPED RICE CEREAL AND POUR IT INTO ITS PAIRED SOLID.

SHADE IN HOW HIGH THE CEREAL FILLED EACH SOLID.

Rectangle Base	Triangle Base	Circle Base
5 cm, 4 cm, 3 cm; $\frac{2}{3}$, $\frac{3}{4}$, $\frac{1}{2}$, 1	5 cm, 4 cm, 3 cm; $\frac{2}{3}$, $\frac{3}{4}$, $\frac{1}{2}$, 1	5 cm, 4 cm, 3 cm; $\frac{2}{3}$, $\frac{3}{4}$, $\frac{1}{2}$, 1

What is the relationship of the volumes of the pointed boxes to their corresponding solids?

A pointed box is a third of its paired solid.

Calculate the volume of each pair of the pyramids and cones.

Rectangle Base		Triangle Base		Circle Base	
Base $l \cdot w = A$	49 cm²	Base $(b \cdot h) \div 2 = A$	24.5 cm²	Base $\pi r^2 = A$	38.5 cm²
Height	6 cm	Height	6 cm	Height	6 cm
Volume: Rectangular Solid	294 cm³	Volume: Triangular Prism	147 cm³	Volume: Cylinder	231 cm³
Volume: Rectangular Based Pyramid	98 cm³	Volume: Triangular Based Pyramid	49 cm³	Volume: Cone	77 cm³

Animation

BBs transferring from pyramids and cones to prisms and cylinders reinforce the one-third factor in the formulas. (A second animation addressing this concept is found in the *Extras* of the accompanying CD.)

Comics

Stresses the one-third relationship of the volume of a triangular-based pyramid to a triangular-based prism with equal bases and heights, also the one-third relationship of the volume of a cone to a cylinder with equal bases and heights.

Demonstrates with physical models how to determine the volume of a solid by layering or referring to other solids.

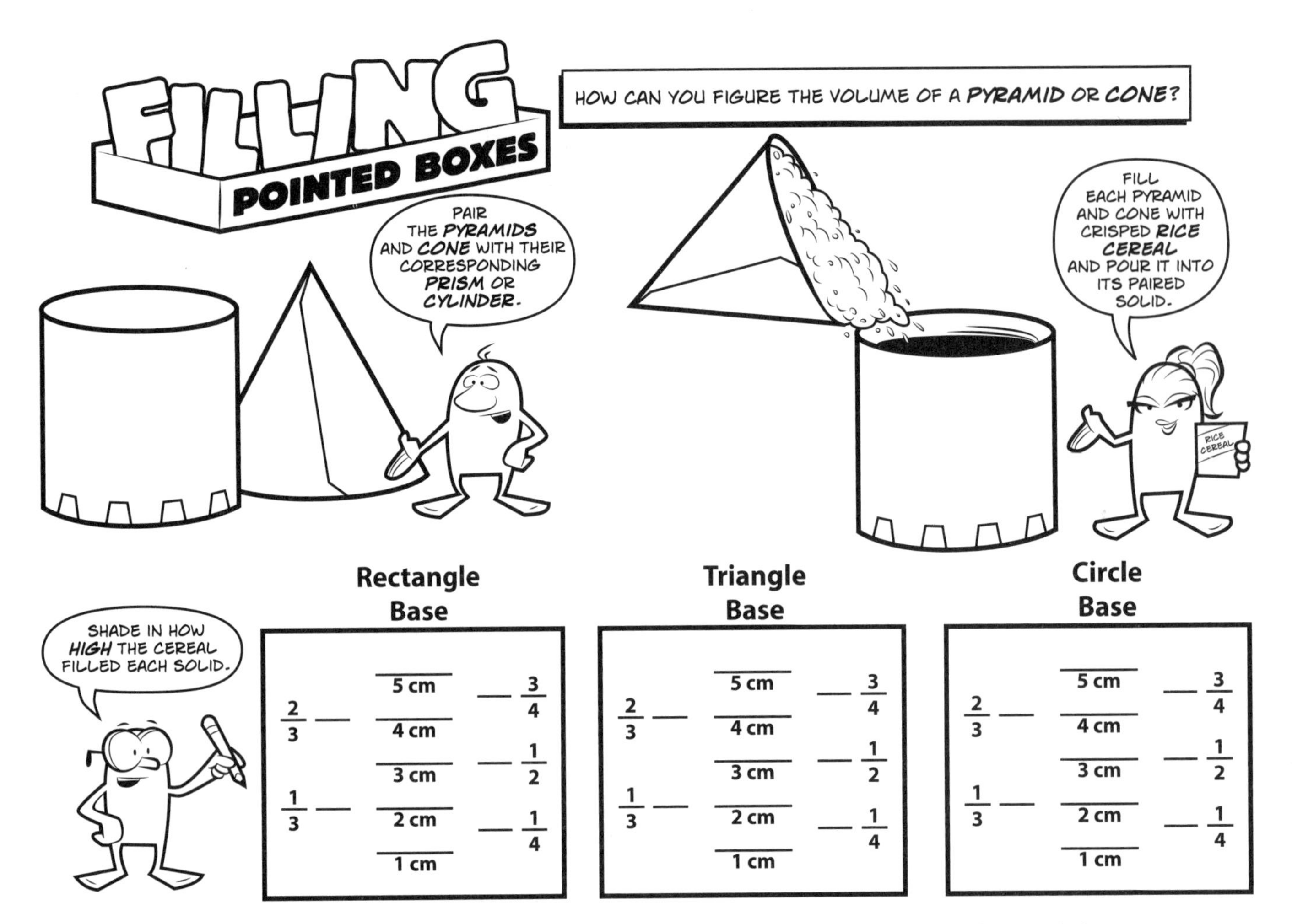

What is the relationship of the volumes of the pointed boxes to their corresponding solids?

Calculate the volume of each pair of the pyramids and cones.

Rectangle Base		Triangle Base		Circle Base	
Base $l \cdot w = A$		Base $(b \cdot h) \div 2 = A$		Base $\pi r^2 = A$	
Height		Height		Height	
Volume: Rectangular Solid		Volume: Triangular Prism		Volume: Cylinder	
Volume: Rectangular Based Pyramid		Volume: Triangular Based Pyramid		Volume: Cone	

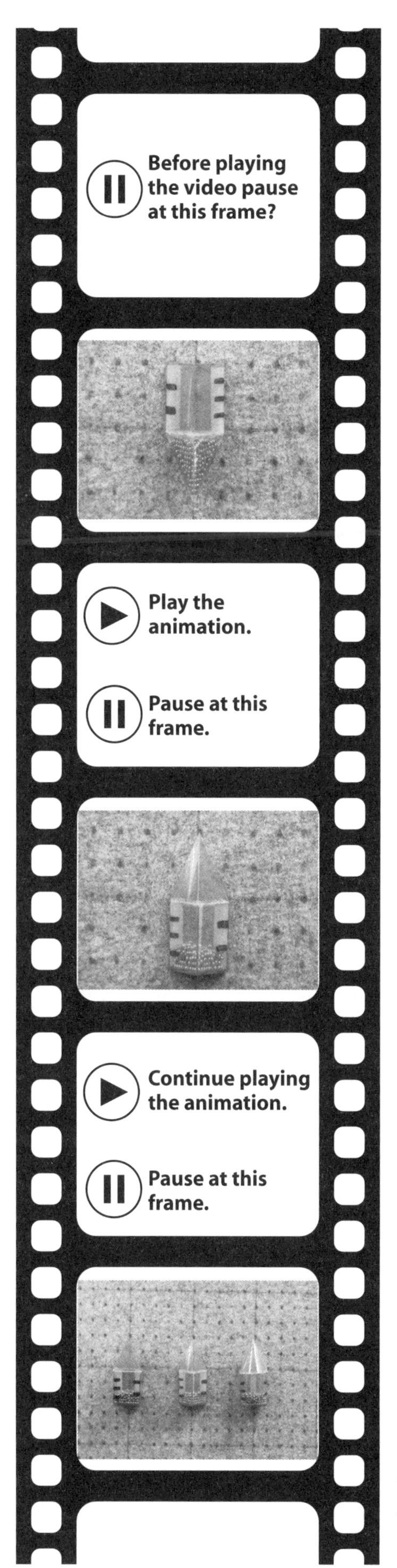

Pouring Pyramids and Cones

What fraction of a prism or cylinder is filled with a pyramid or cone with a congruent base and height?

What measurements are the same in this cylinder and cone?

Predict what fraction of the cylinder will be filled by the bb's in the cone. Explain your prediction.

What fraction of the cylinder was filled with bb's from the cone?

How do the volume of the cone and cylinder compare?

What fraction of the prisms and cylinder are filled with bb's from the pyramids and cone?

How do the volumes of the pyramids and cones compare to prisms and cylinders with congruent bases and heights?

The general formula for a prism or cylinder is (V = Bh). How would you change the formula to find the volume of a pyramid or cone?

MEASUREMENT OF PRISMS, PYRAMIDS, CYLINDERS, AND CONES
ESSENTIAL MATH SERIES
Filling Pointed Boxes
THINGS TO LOOK FOR:
1. WHY CAN'T WE FIND THE VOLUME OF A PYRAMID BY FILLING IT WITH CUBES LIKE WE DID FOR A PRISM?
2. HOW DOES KNOWING THE FORMULA FOR THE VOLUME OF A PRISM HELP US FIND THE VOLUME OF A PYRAMID WITH THE SAME BASE AND HEIGHT?
LET'S TALK ABOUT WHAT WE DID TO FIGURE OUT HOW TO FIND THE VOLUME OF A PYRAMID OR CONE.
IT WAS REALLY DIFFERENT FROM THE WAY WE FOUND THE VOLUME OF THE OTHER SOLIDS.
YEAH, IT WAS COOL! WE POURED CEREAL FROM A PYRAMID INTO A PRISM, OR FROM A CONE INTO A CYLINDER. CEREAL'S MY FAVORITE.
WHY DIDN'T WE DO IT WITH LAYERS OF CUBES LIKE WE DID WITH THE PRISMS AND CYLINDERS?
LET'S THINK ABOUT THAT. THERE'S A GOOD REASON WE CAN'T DO IT WITH LAYERS OF CUBES.
I WANT YOU TO LOOK AT THIS SQUARE-BASED PYRAMID. THE BASE IS 7 BY 7 JUST LIKE THE PRISM IN THE PREVIOUS ACTIVITY.
WHAT WOULD HAPPEN IF WE TRIED TO FIT A LAYER OF CUBES INTO THIS PYRAMID?
IT WON'T FIT BECAUSE THE FACES OF THE PYRAMID ARE SLOPED IN FROM THE BASE.
THAT'S RIGHT, ELORA.
IF WE WANTED TO FIT A LAYER OF CUBES INTO THE PYRAMID, WE WOULD HAVE TO MAKE ANGLED CUTS ON ALL OF THE EDGE CUBES.
YOU SAW THE FIRST LAYER, HERE'S WHAT TWO LAYERS WOULD LOOK LIKE.
1
OH, MAN. THAT LOOKS HARD. HOW ARE WE GOING TO CUT THE CUBES ACCURATELY ENOUGH?
THAT'S THE POINT--YOU CAN'T!
REDMOND, DO YOU SEE WHY WE DON'T USE LAYERS OF CUBES TO FIND THE VOLUME OF PYRAMIDS AND CONES?
YUP! THAT MAKES SENSE. I LIKE POURING CEREAL BACK AND FORTH.
OKAY, SO HOW DID YOU DO THIS POURING, AND WHAT DID YOU FIND OUT?
THE BASES OF THE SQUARE-BASED PRISM FROM BEFORE AND THE PYRAMID ARE CONGRUENT.
THAT MEANS THE BASES HAVE THE SAME AREA. THEY'RE BOTH 49 SQUARE CENTIMETERS, ALSO BOTH THE PRISM AND THE PYRAMID HAVE A HEIGHT OF 6.
THE SAME THING HAPPENS WITH THE TRIANGULAR PRISM AND PYRAMID, AND WITH THE CYLINDER AND CONE.
THEY ALL HAVE A HEIGHT OF 6 CENTIMETERS, AND THE AREAS OF THE BASES OF THE TRIANGULAR PRISM AND PYRAMID ARE THE SAME, AND THE AREA OF THE BASE OF THE CYLINDER IS THE SAME AS THE CONE.
24.5 SQUARE CENTIMETERS
24.5 SQUARE CENTIMETERS
38.5 SQUARE CENTIMETERS
38.5 SQUARE CENTIMETERS
SO, FIRST WE FILLED THE PYRAMIDS AND THE CONE WITH CEREAL.
AND THEN WE POURED THE CEREAL FROM EACH ONE INTO THE PROPER PRISMS AND CYLINDER. FOR EACH ONE, THE CEREAL CAME UP TO THE 1/3 MARK.
OF COURSE IT DID. THAT MEANS THAT THE PYRAMIDS AND THE CONE HOLD 1/3 AS MUCH AS THE PRISMS AND THE CYLINDER.
OKAY, SO, WHAT IS THE FORMULA FOR THE VOLUME OF THE PYRAMIDS AND THE CONE?
2

WELL, THE FORMULA FOR THE VOLUME OF THE PRISMS AND CYLINDER IS THE AREA OF THE BASE TIMES THE HEIGHT.
SO, THEN, FOR THE PYRAMIDS AND CONE, IT WOULD JUST BE 1/3 TIMES THE AREA OF THE BASE TIMES THE HEIGHT.
WHOA. HOLD ON. DOES THE SAME FORMULA WORK FOR BOTH THE PYRAMIDS AND THE CONES?
THE ONLY REAL DIFFERENCE BETWEEN PYRAMIDS AND CONES IS THE SHAPE OF THEIR BASES. ONCE YOU FIGURE OUT THE AREA OF THE BASE, THE FORMULA IS THE SAME FOR BOTH.
LIKE, IF IT'S A CONE YOU'D USE π • r² TO FIND THE AREA OF THE BASE, OR IT'S A PYRAMID WITH A TRIANGLE BASE, YOU'D USE 1/2 • b • h TO FIND THE AREA.
V = 1/3 • B • h
r = 3.5
d = 7
B = π • r²
B = 1/2 • b • h
BASE
7
7
6
10
7
THE BASE OF A PYRAMID COULD ALSO BE A SQUARE OR A RECTANGLE.
SO, ONCE YOU HAVE THE AREA OF THE BASE, YOU MULTIPLY IT TIMES THE HEIGHT AND DIVIDE BY 3 TO GET THE VOLUME!

What is the relationship of pyramids and cubes that have the same size base and height? How can you use this relationship to find the volume of a pyramid?

Pyramids and cones always are one-third of the volume of a prism or cylinder that has a congruent base and equal height. Students will validate this observation by building three congruent square-based pyramids. They will then fill a cube of equal length, width, and height to the pyramids.

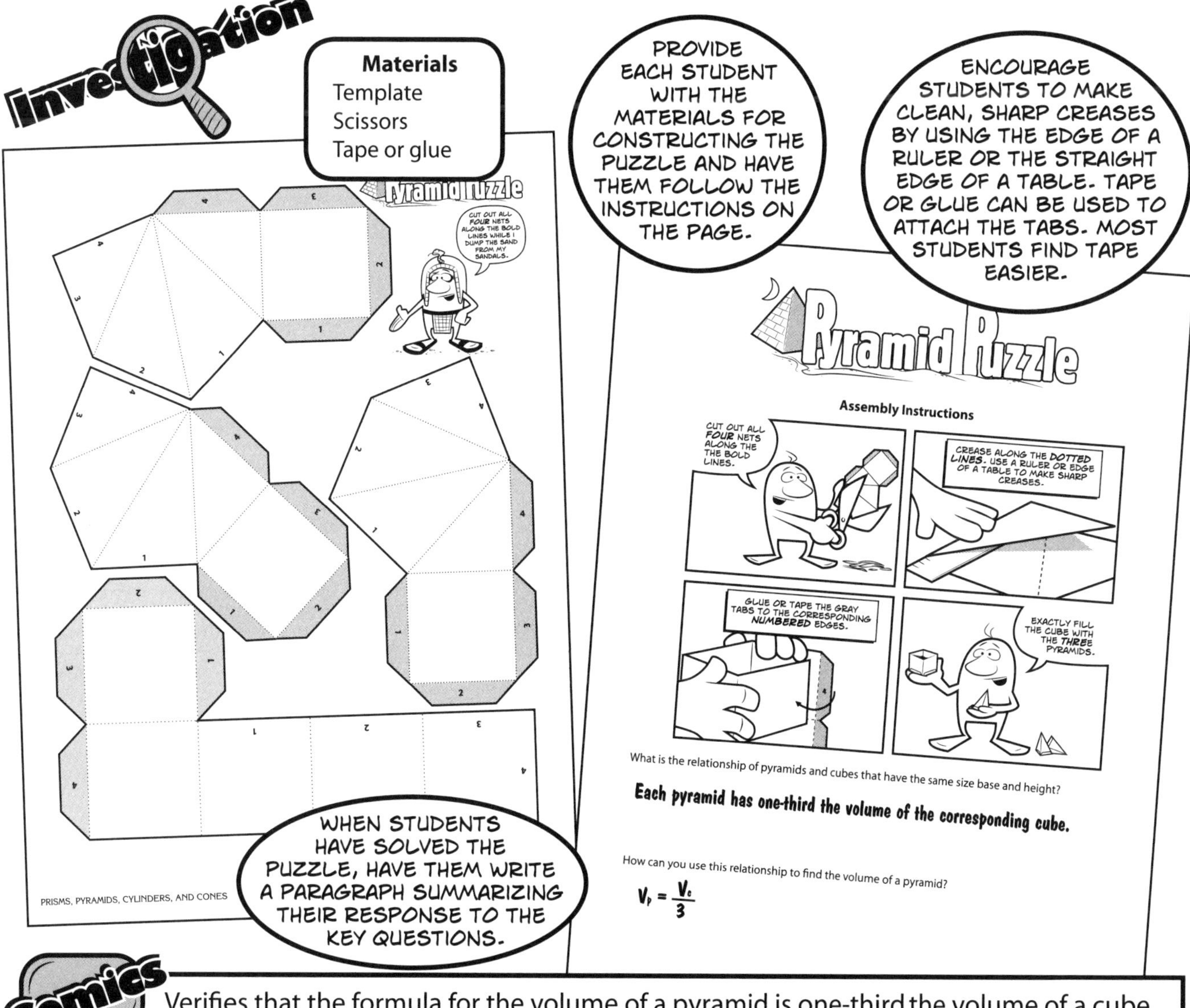

Verifies that the formula for the volume of a pyramid is one-third the volume of a cube with the same height and base.

Shows students how surface area and volume are applied in real-world problems.

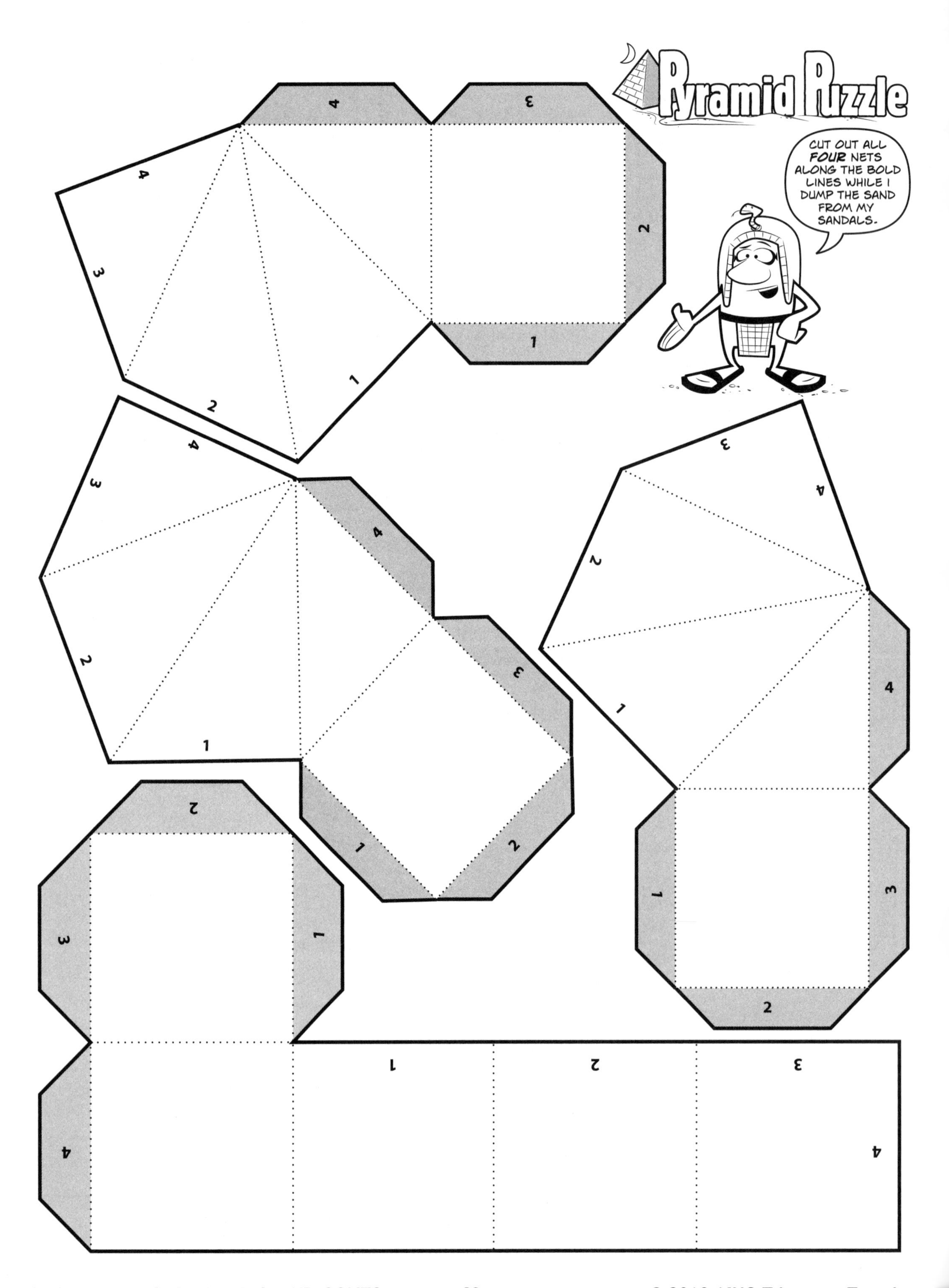
Pyramid Puzzle
CUT OUT ALL FOUR NETS ALONG THE BOLD LINES WHILE I DUMP THE SAND FROM MY SANDALS.

Assembly Instructions

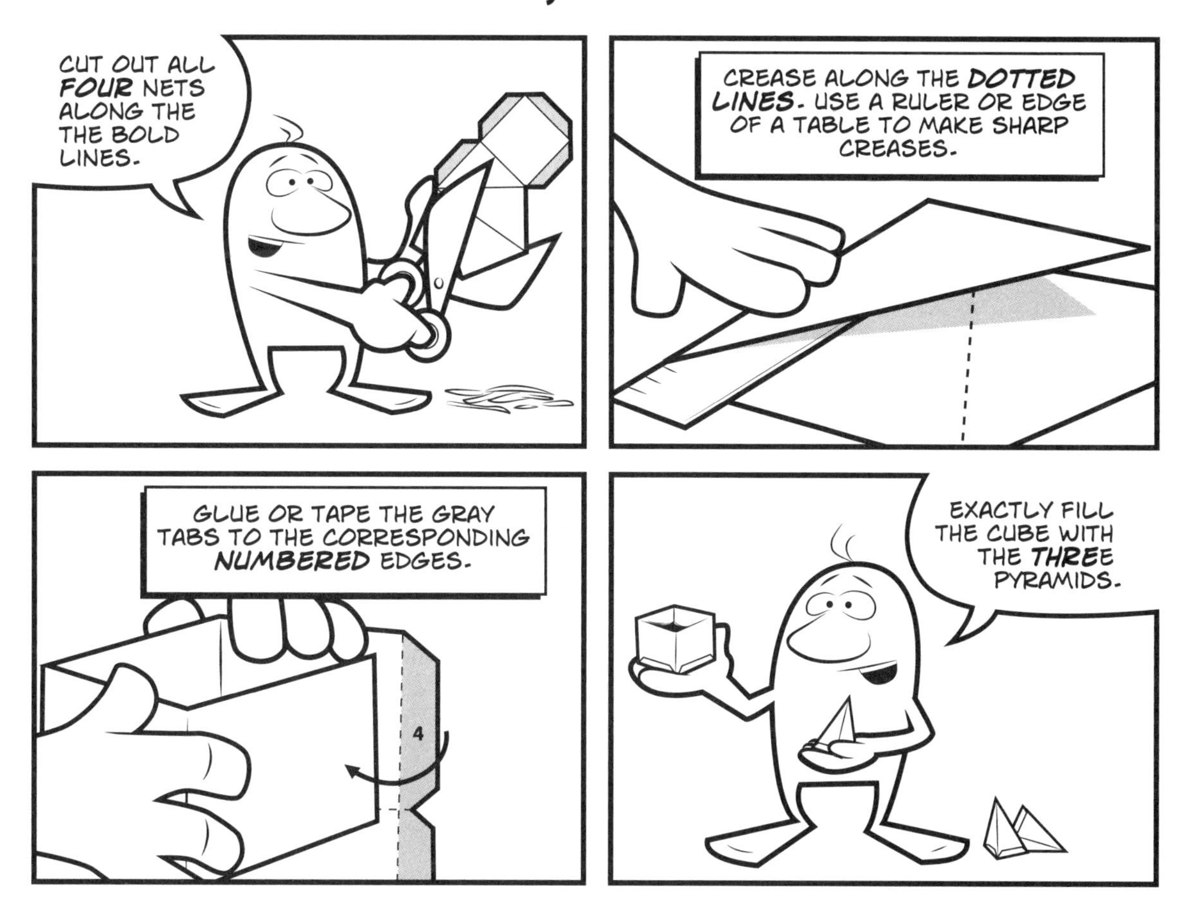

What is the relationship of pyramids and cubes that have the same size base and height?

How can you use this relationship to find the volume of a pyramid?

MEASUREMENT OF PRISMS, PYRAMIDS, CYLINDERS, AND CONES
ESSENTIAL MATH SERIES
PYRAMID PUZZLE
THINGS TO LOOK FOR:
1. HOW DOES THIS PUZZLE HELP YOU UNDERSTAND THE FORMULA FOR THE VOLUME OF A PYRAMID?
LET'S TALK ABOUT THE PUZZLE YOU JUST MADE.
YOU WERE GIVEN THREE NETS THAT YOU FORMED INTO PYRAMIDS, AND YOU WERE GIVEN A FOURTH NET THAT YOU FORMED INTO AN OPEN CUBE.
ONCE THEY WERE ALL BUILT, THEY LOOKED SOMETHING LIKE THIS.
WHAT DID YOU NOTICE ABOUT THE THREE PYRAMIDS?
THEY'RE EXACTLY THE SAME. I GUESS THAT MEANS THEY'RE CONGRUENT, IS THAT RIGHT?
YES, THEY ARE! REMEMBER, CLASS, CONGRUENT MEANS THEY ARE THE SAME SIZE AND THE SAME SHAPE.
IF THEY'RE CONGRUENT, THEN JUST ABOUT EVERYTHING ABOUT THEM IS EXACTLY THE SAME. THEY EVEN HAVE THE SAME VOLUMES.
NOW, WHAT IS THE SHAPE OF THE BASE OF EACH OF THE PYRAMIDS?
IT'S A 4 BY 4 SQUARE. ALSO, THE HEIGHT OF EACH PYRAMID IS 4, TOO.
THE CUBE WE BUILT WAS 4 BY 4 BY 4, TOO. THAT'S WHY THE PYRAMIDS WOULD FIT INTO IT.
YEAH, THAT'S ALL THERE WAS TO THE PUZZLE. IT WAS PRETTY EASY.
1
WE JUST HAD TO FIT ALL THREE OF THE PYRAMIDS INTO THE CUBE.
OKAY, SO HOW DOES THE VOLUME OF ONE OF THE PYRAMIDS COMPARE TO THE VOLUME OF THE CUBE?
THE VOLUME OF THE PYRAMID IS 1/3 THE VOLUME OF THE CUBE.
IT'S LIKE THE CUBE IS DIVIDED UP INTO THREE EQUAL PARTS. EACH PART, OR PYRAMID, IS 1/3 OF THE CUBE.
WE ALREADY KNEW THAT EACH PYRAMID WAS 1/3 OF THE VOLUME OF THE CUBE. THAT'S WHAT WE DID IN THE LAST ACTIVITY.
YOU'RE RIGHT, MARK, BUT HOW DID WE FIGURE THAT OUT IN THE LAST ACTIVITY?
WELL, WE FILLED A PYRAMID WITH CEREAL AND POURED IT INTO THE CUBE.
THE CEREAL CAME UP TO THE 1/3 MARK IN THE CUBE.
AND WHEN WE POURED ALL THREE PYRAMIDS INTO THE CUBE, IT FILLED IT!
I GET IT! THE PUZZLE IS JUST ANOTHER WAY TO SHOW THE SAME THING.
RIGHT, IT'S ANOTHER WAY TO SHOW THAT THE VOLUME OF A PYRAMID IS 1/3 THE VOLUME OF A CUBE WITH THE SAME BASE AND HEIGHT.
THAT'S COOL, CAN YOU DO THAT FOR ANY PRISM? CAN YOU PUT THREE PYRAMIDS TOGETHER TO MAKE THE PRISM?
NO, A CUBE IS THE ONLY PRISM WHERE THREE CONGRUENT PYRAMIDS WILL EXACTLY FIT INSIDE IT.
WE DID THE PUZZLE TO GIVE US ONE MORE WAY TO THINK ABOUT THIS IDEA THAT THE VOLUME OF A PYRAMID IS ALWAYS 1/3 OF THE VOLUME OF A PRISM WITH THE SAME BASE AND HEIGHT.
IT MAKES TOTAL SENSE NOW!
GOOD! GREAT JOB, CLASS!
2

Measurement of Prisms, Pyramids, Cylinders, and Cones Assessment

Both assessments are based in contexts that are familiar to students. Rather than ask for surface area, the question asks for amount of aluminum sheet or foil. Volume is asked as how much soda or juice in the container. The problems are presented at a representational level. Allowing access to the solids that were constructed during the unit gives students something to refer to when doing their work.

This is a straight forward calculation of surface area and volume. In assessing understanding, look for the big ideas along with demonstration of calculations.

Surface Area—How much aluminum sheet?

Surface area is the sum of all the surfaces. A cylinder is made of two circles and a rectangle with the length the circumference of the circle.

2 circles:	pi times radius square	$3.14(4^2) = 50.\ 24$	$2(50.24) = 100.48$
1 rectangle:	circumference times height	$3.14(8) \cdot 14$	$25.12(14) = 351.68$
		Total	$452.16 \approx 452\ cm^2$

Volume—How much soda?

Volume is base or how much is in a layer times height. A cylinder has a circle for a base.

Base:	pi times radius square	$3.14(4^2) = 50.\ 24\ cm^2$
Volume:	Base · height	$50.24cm^2 \cdot 14\ cm = 703.36 \approx 703\ cm^3$

This assessment is more involved in that unknown dimensions are found by working backwards. In assessing understanding, look for the big ideas along with demonstration of correct calculations.

Volume—How much juice?

Volume is base or how much is in a layer times height. A cylinder has a circle for a base.

Base:	pi times radius square	$3.14(3.25^2) \approx 33.17\ cm^2$
Volume:	Base · height	$33.17 \cdot 8 = 265.36 \approx 265\ cm^3$

Height—How high do you make a can to get the needed volume?

Work backwards from the volume by dividing by Base.

Base:	triangle: (b · h)÷2	$(6 \cdot 8) \div 2 = 24\ cm^2$
Volume:	Volume = Base · height	$265 = 24 \cdot h$
		$265 \div 24 = h \approx 11\ cm$

Surface Area—How much aluminum foil?

Surface is the sum of all the surfaces. This prism is made of two triangles and three rectangles.

2 triangles:	triangle: (b · h)÷2	$(6 \cdot 8) \div 2 = 24\ cm^2$	$2(24)$	$= 48\ cm^2$
1 rectangle:	base · height	$6 \cdot 11 = 66$		$= 66\ cm^2$
1 rectangle:	base · height	$8 \cdot 11 = 88$		$= 88\ cm^2$
1 rectangle:	base · height	$10 \cdot 11 = 110$		$= 110\ cm^2$
		Total		$= 312\ cm^2$

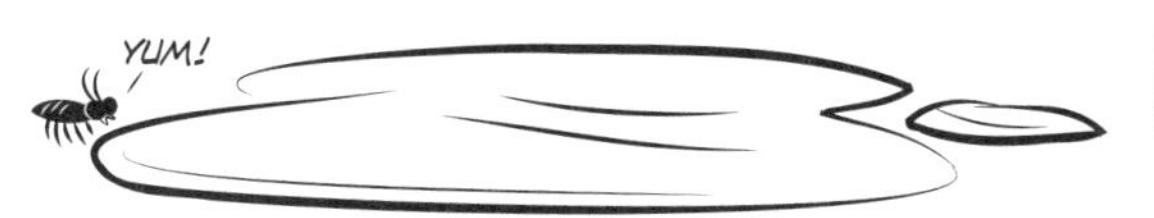

Soda Can Development

The production team has designed this soda can. Determine the amount of aluminum sheet needed to form the can and the amount of soda it will hold.

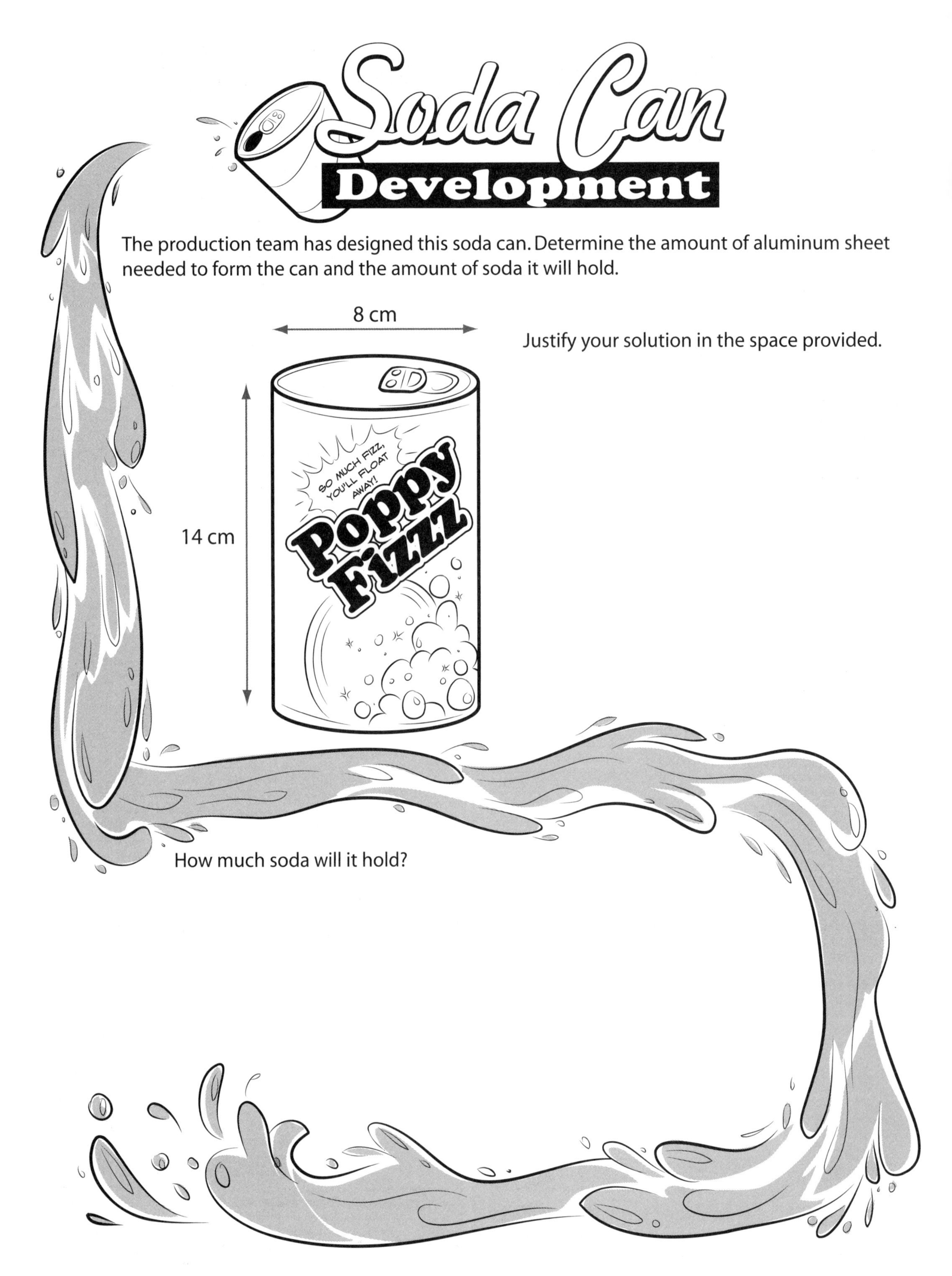

Justify your solution in the space provided.

How much soda will it hold?

Juice Box Design

To change the company's image and for more efficient packaging, a juice producer is going to switch from the present cylinder to a triangular prism box.

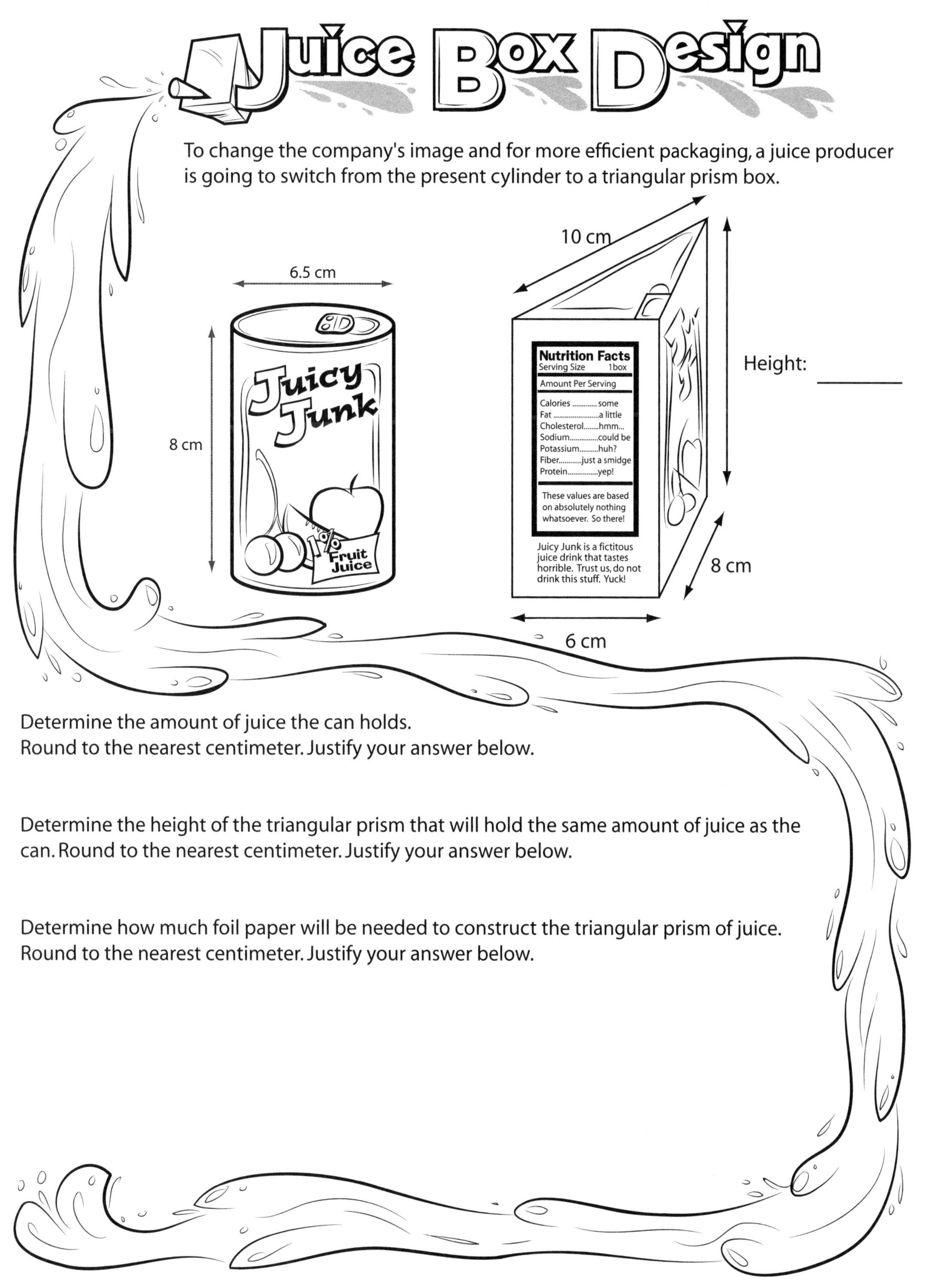

Determine the amount of juice the can holds.
Round to the nearest centimeter. Justify your answer below.

Determine the height of the triangular prism that will hold the same amount of juice as the can. Round to the nearest centimeter. Justify your answer below.

Determine how much foil paper will be needed to construct the triangular prism of juice.
Round to the nearest centimeter. Justify your answer below.

THIS PAGE IS GOOD FOR REFERENCE

GLOSSARY

THERE'S A LOT OF GOOD INFO DOWN THERE!

CONE
A solid that has a circle as a base and its lateral surface comes to a point.

CYLINDER
A solid that has identical circular bases (top and bottom) that are parallel to each other. The surface that connects the bases is curved and is called the lateral surface.

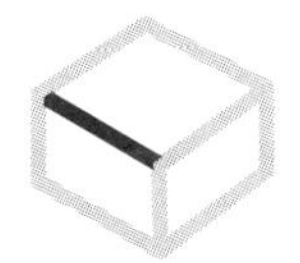

EDGE
A line segment where two faces meet.

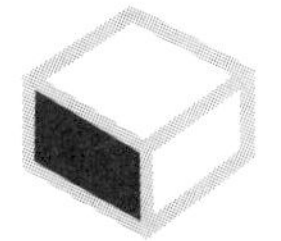

FACE
A polygon that forms a wall of a solid.

POLYHEDRON
A solid with flat faces and straight edges.

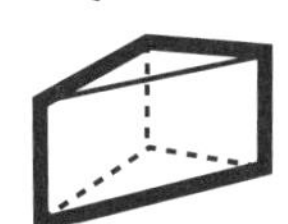

PRISM
A polyhedron that has two identical sides opposite and parallel of each other. The lateral sides are all parallelograms.

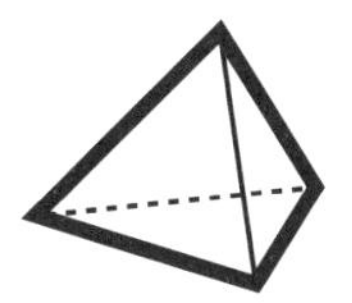

PYRAMID
A polyhedron that has a polygon on the bottom called the base. The lateral sides of a pyramid all come to a point. All the lateral sides of a pyramid are triangles.

SOLID
A three-dimensional container that takes up space.

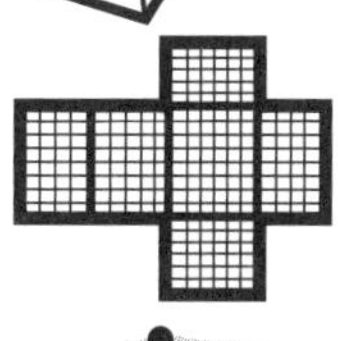

SURFACE AREA
The number of squares needed to cover the surface of a solid.

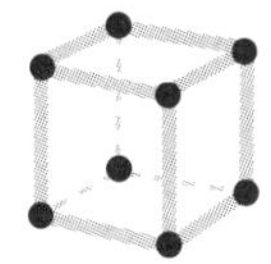

VERTEX
A corner where three or more edges meet.

VOLUME
The space inside a solid. It is measured by the number of cubes that would fill it.

Standards from Guiding Documents

Project 2061 Benchmarks

- *Length can be thought of as unit lengths joined together, area as a collection of unit squares, and volume as a set of unit cubes.*
- *Areas of irregular shapes can be found by dividing them into squares and triangles.*

American Association for the Advancement of Science
Benchmarks for Science Literacy
Oxford University Press. New York. 1993.

NCTM Standards 2000*

- *Understand, select, and use units of appropriate size and type to measure angles, perimeter, area, surface area, and volume*
- *Use geometric models to solve problems in other areas of mathematics, such as number and measurement*
- *Develop, understand, and use formulas to find the area of rectangles and related triangles and parallelograms*
- *Develop strategies for estimating the perimeters, areas, and volumes of irregular shapes*

Reprinted with permission from
Principles and Standards for School Mathematics 2000
by the National Council of Teachers of Mathematics

Using Comics to Teach Math

The *Essential Math* units contain comics. They generally are used to clarify and review the class investigation.

Rationale

Comics were chosen for several reasons. First, students are very comfortable with the comic format and are much more motivated to read the material because of the medium. Secondly, it has been found that material that is written in comic format is more easily understood than when the same information is delivered in narrative format. This may be true for several reasons:

- Comics combine images and words to help students make sense of the concepts and relationships that are the focus of an activity.
- Comics are more casual so academic vocabulary can be understood through visual clues and common language.
- Comics by nature deliver the same information with fewer words. As a result, the author must be brief and clear and must craft the dialogue carefully.
- Comics are naturally sequential. Each frame is a snapshot. This provides a progressive development of ideas with a chance for the reader to stop at each point to comprehend what is being said.
- The visual nature of the comics allows them to reinforce the conceptual understanding introduced in the investigation. The affective and cognitive benefits of comics make them an excellent resource for reading in the content area of math.

Possible Usage

Directed Reading: The comics may be distributed to be read individually either at school or home. Direct the students to do pre-reading by reading the summary questions and scanning the comic. When students have completed the reading, have a class discussion on the summary questions.

Reader's Theater: Assign students different characters in the comic and have them do an oral presentation. If time allows, split the class into teams to practice reading the script and then give multiple performances, or assign each group a page to read. Engage more students by providing word cards of key words. Have non-reading students hold up the cards whenever their word is said. Be sure to have a discussion after reading the comic that includes the summary questions.

Teaching Scripts: While time constraints may prevent the use of the comics with students, the teacher can glean the finer points of the concepts and teaching strategies from them. The comic provides a script of how this might be presented to the class and how a discussion might be encouraged.

Formats

The comics can be copied for the students or displayed on a computer or projector. The paper copies can be made from the book or pdf files on the compact disc. The pdf files come in a full-page version or the more efficient two-page version found in the book. For viewing with a computer, there is a full-page view. When using a projector, choose the slide show version with large easily read frames.

Using Animations to Teach Math

Each *Essential Math* unit contains animations that provide culminating experiences for big ideas. As a visual medium, animations provide a very powerful tool for understanding and memory. If a picture is worth a thousand words, an animation is worth many times more.

The Dynamic Nature of an animation allows the viewer to make connections and build relationships not available with a static picture. As the animation runs, the student should be asked to identify what actions they see happening, the relationships within those events, and how the animation relates to prior experiences in the unit.

A Usage Guide is provided for each animation as a student record page. It can be used as a guide for class discussion. It may be used as a record sheet for students or may be used by the teachers as a guide for when to pause the animation and elicit class discussion.

The animations are available on the compact disc and need to be played through a computer. The player allows for pausing and frame-by-frame movement. They are best viewed by a class using a projector, but may be displayed on a single monitor.

The Story of Measurement of Prisms, Cylinders, Pyramids, and Cones

The focus of this unit is on measuring three-dimensional shapes—prisms, cylinders, pyramids, and cones—called geometric solids. The word *solid* in this context simply means three-dimensional. The measurement of these shapes involves length, area, and volume. Length units are line segments, area units are squares, and volume units are cubes.

Prisms

A prism is a geometric solid that has **one pair of opposite faces** that are congruent and parallel and are called **bases** of the prism. The remaining faces are **rectangular shapes** and are called **lateral faces.** The bases of a prism can be any polygonal shapes, but this unit focuses on square- and triangular-based prisms. The perimeter of a base is equal to the sum of the lengths of the lateral faces. This makes sense because the lateral faces wrap around the bases.

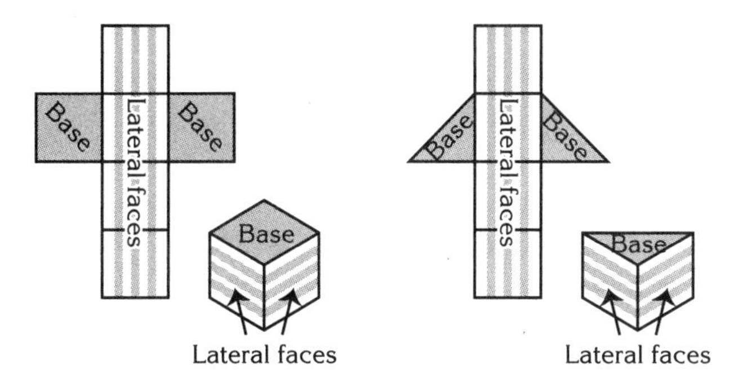

Cylinders

A cylinder is like a prism in that it has a **pair of opposite faces called bases** that are parallel and congruent. A cylinder is different from a prism in that its **bases are circular**; and it has a **one-piece curved lateral surface**. Notice that the rectangular shape that becomes the curved lateral surface of the cylinder has a width that is the height of the cylinder, and a length that is equal to the circumference of the base because the lateral surface wraps around the bases.

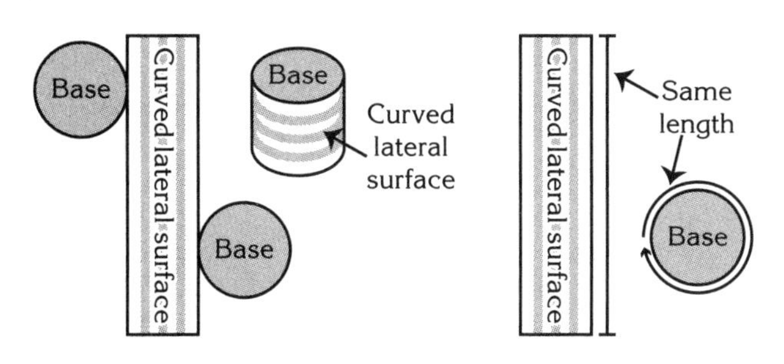

Pyramids

A pyramid is a geometric solid with four or more polygonal faces. One of these faces is called the base of the pyramid and can be any polygonal shape. A pyramid has only one base. The **remaining faces of the pyramid are all triangular shaped** and are called **lateral faces.** The lateral faces of a pyramid all come together at a common point that is a special vertex called the **apex**, which is opposite the base.

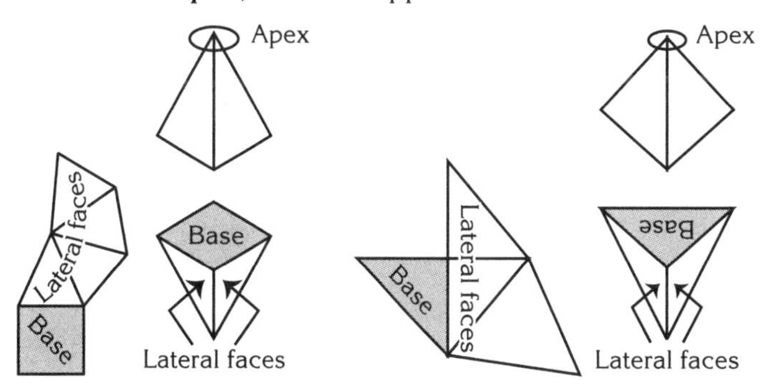

Cones

What a pyramid is to a prism, a cone is to a cylinder. Like a pyramid, a cone has **one base,** but it is a **circular shape** like the bases of a cylinder. A cone has a **one-piece lateral surface that is slanted** and comes to an apex. While the lateral surface of a cylinder is a rectangular shape, **the lateral surface of a cone is a portion of a circular shape** and is called a **sector of a circle.**

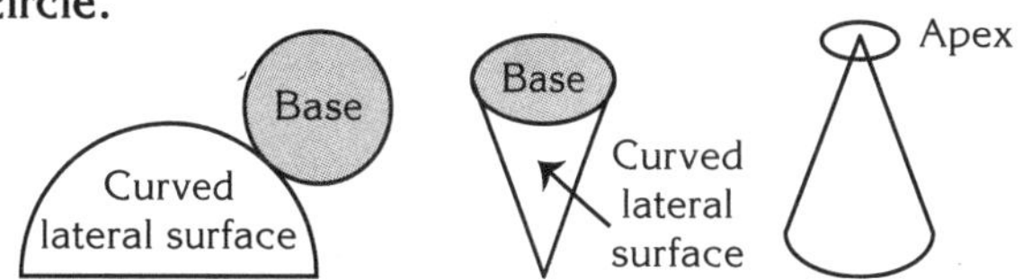

For the cone that students build in this unit, the sector of the circle is actually a semi-circular shape; it is half of a circle. (This was chosen for ease of construction and calculations.)

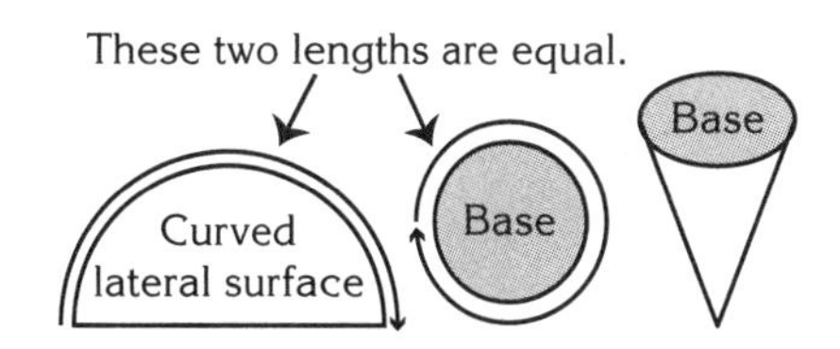

The sector of a circle that forms the lateral surface of the cone does not have to be a semi-circle. It could be less than half or more than half of a circular shape. What is important is that the length of the arc of the sector must be equal to the circumference of the circle.

Look at these next two cones and compare them to the previously pictured cone. The diameter of the base of each of the three cones is the same. When the lateral surface is less than a semi-circle, its radius has to be longer than the diameter of the base. When the lateral surface is more than a semi-circle, the radius has to be shorter. The heights of the three cones also vary. When the lateral surface is less than a semi-circle, the cone is taller; and when it is more than a semi-circle, the cone is shorter.

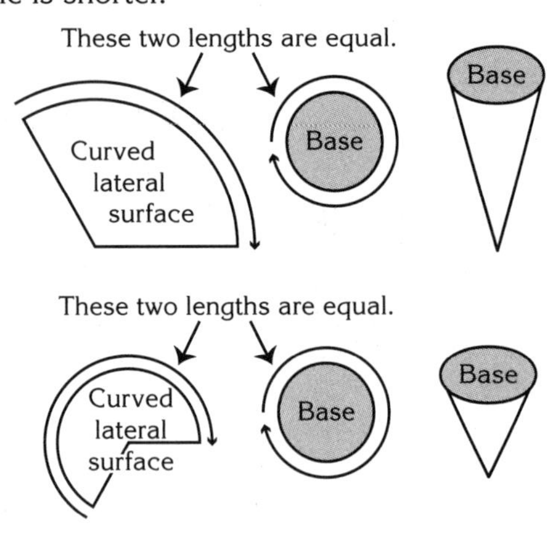

Surface Area

Measuring Surface Area of Prisms and Pyramids

The three-dimensional shapes in this unit start out as two-dimensional nets. For the prisms and pyramids, these nets are made up of polygons, each of which is connected to another along a common side. When folded up and formed into a prism or pyramid, these common sides become the edges of the solid shape, and the polygonal shapes become the faces. The **surface area of a prism or pyramid is the sum of the areas of each of its faces.** Remember that the polygonal shapes that were joined together to form the nets are exactly the same polygonal shapes that are the faces of the prism or pyramid.

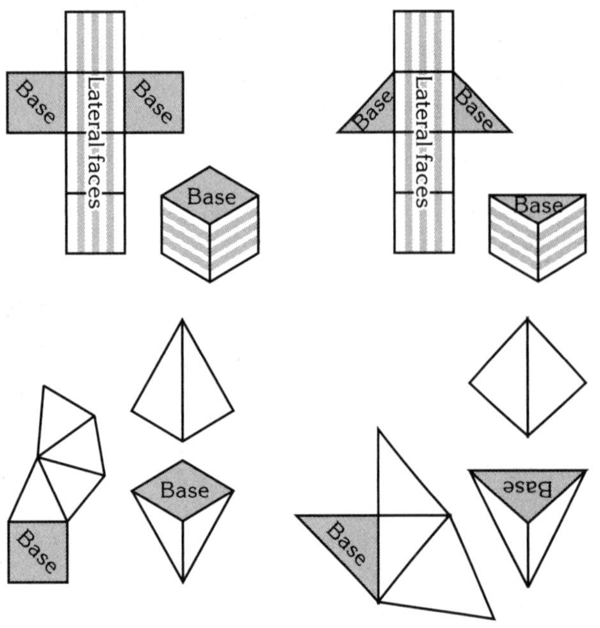

To find the surface area of either of these shapes, we simply have to find the area of each face and then add them up. The measurements for the triangular-based pyramid are shown below. Students can either measure the faces of the pyramid or measure the triangular shapes as they appear in the net. Three of the triangular faces are right triangles so that one of the sides of those triangles is the base and the other the height of those triangles. (**SA** is the symbol for surface area.)

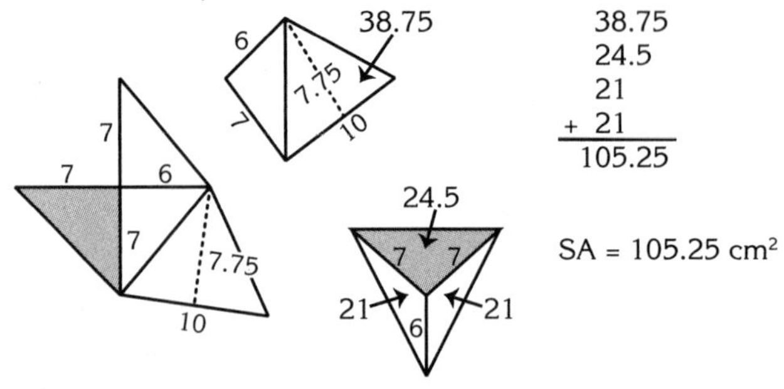

Measuring Surface Area of Cylinders

For a cylinder, the net consists of two circular shapes and one rectangular shape. When formed into a cylinder, these three shapes become the two circular bases and the curved lateral surface. **The surface area of a cylinder is the sum of the areas of the two bases and the curved lateral surface.** We can measure the diameter or radius of the circular bases and use the formula πr^2 for finding their areas. The **lateral surface** that wraps around the bases is a **rectangle** with **length equal to the circumference of a base** and **width equal to the height of the cylinder.** In order to visualize what the curved lateral surface looks like, it is helpful to have the net available. In fact, it is probably easier to find the surface area of the cylinder by simply finding the areas of the two circular shapes and the rectangle (lateral surface) as they appear in the net.

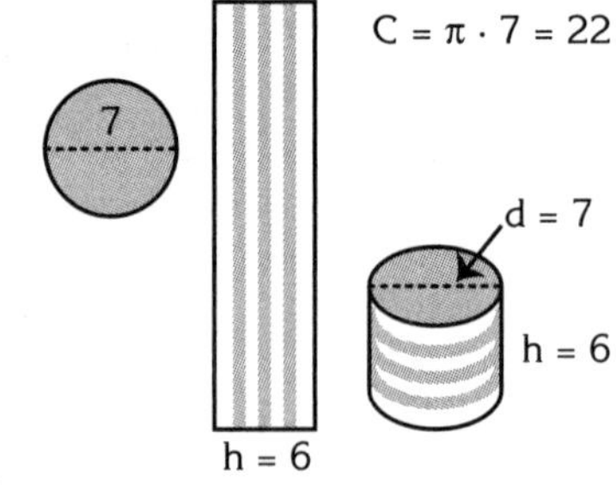

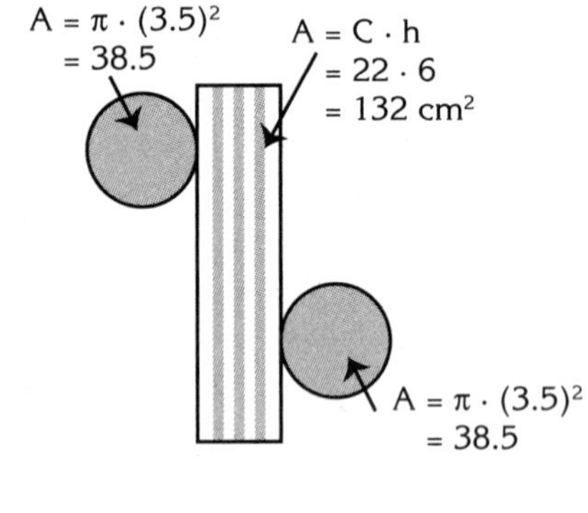

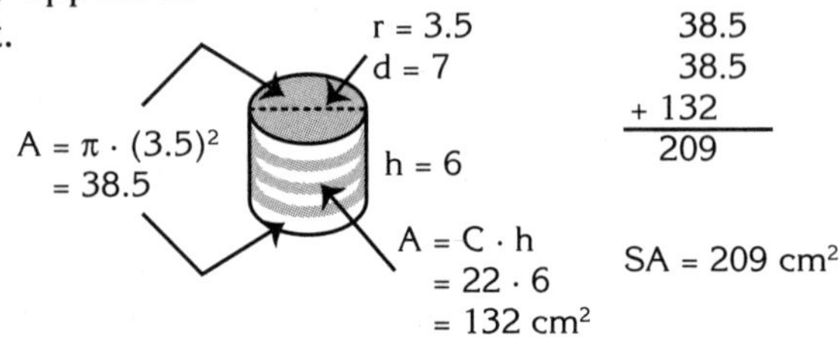

Measuring the Surface Area of Cones

The net for a cone is made of two pieces. These are a circular shape that becomes the base and a sector of a different circle that becomes the curved and slated lateral surface. To make finding the areas somewhat easier, the cone that the students explore has a lateral surface that is a semi-circular shape.

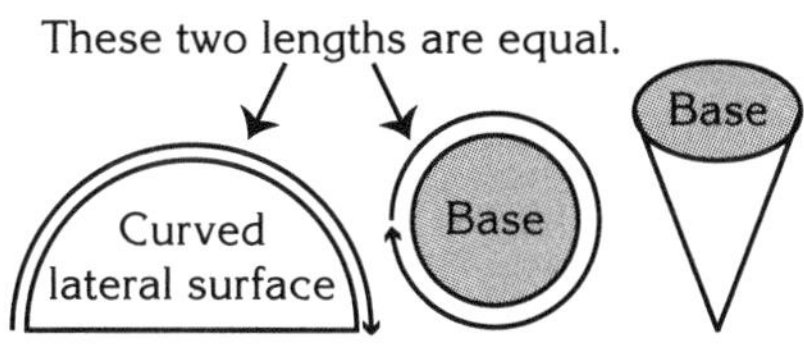

It is important to notice that the diameter of the sector is 14 cm and the diameter of the base of the cone is 7 cm. If students calculate the circumference of a circle with a diameter of 7, they should find that the circumference is about 22. If they did the same for a diameter of 14, they would find that the circumference is about 44. In this way, students should see that half way around a circle with a diameter of 14 is equal to all the way around a circle with a diameter of 7. That's important, of course, for the lateral surface of the cone to exactly fit on the base.

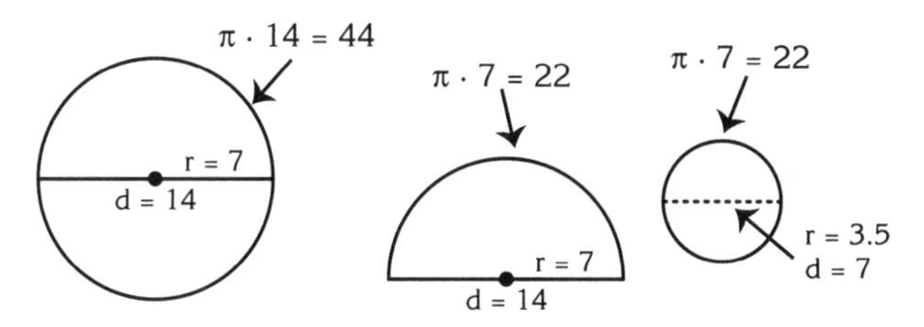

With this background and these measurements, the next step is to find the surface area of this cone. The surface area of a cone is the sum of the areas of the circular base and the lateral surface. Students will use the area formula for circles, πr^2, to find the area of the base, which has a radius of 3.5. Then they will find the area of the lateral surface, which in this case is a half circle with a radius of 7. This is one-half the area of a circle with a radius of 7, so students can simply find the area of that circle using πr^2 again, and then divide by 2. The sum of these two areas is the surface area of the cone.

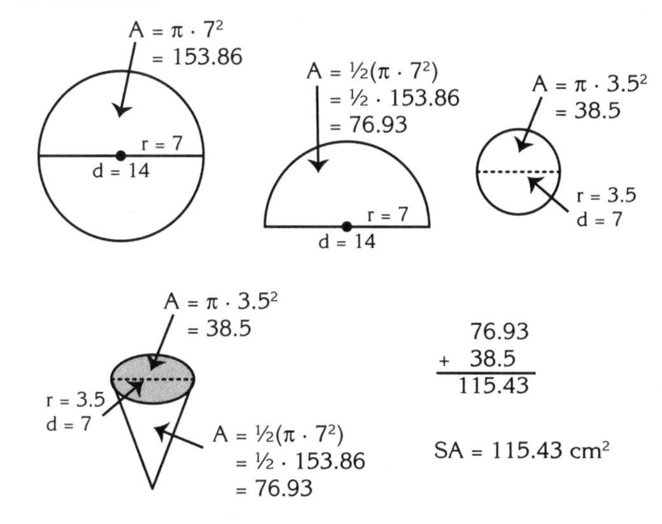

Volumes

Measuring Volumes of Prisms and Cylinders

Volume is a measure of filling. The **unit of measurement is a cube,** which may be a cubic inch, a cubic centimeter, or any other cubic unit. In this unit a cubic centimeter will be the unit of volume measure. The key idea involved in finding the volume of prisms and cylinders is to think about filling them with layers of cubes.

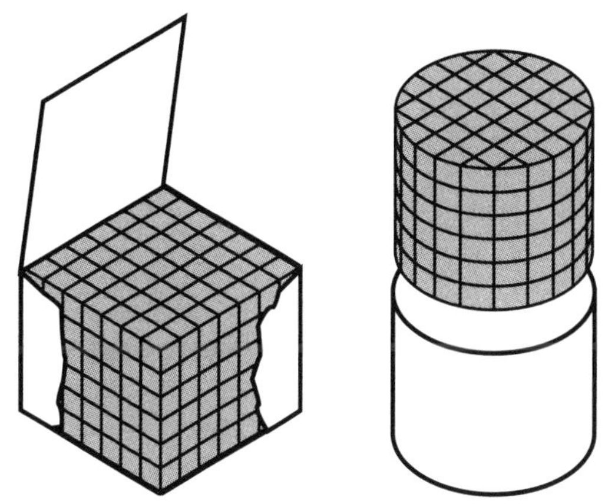

Volume of a Square-Based Prism

The square-based prism is a good place to start because students can literally pack cubes into the prism and see how many cubes are needed to fill it. The base of the square-based prism is 7 cm by 7 cm. Since a cube will fit on top of each square unit of the base, the number of cubes in a layer must be exactly the same as the area of the base.

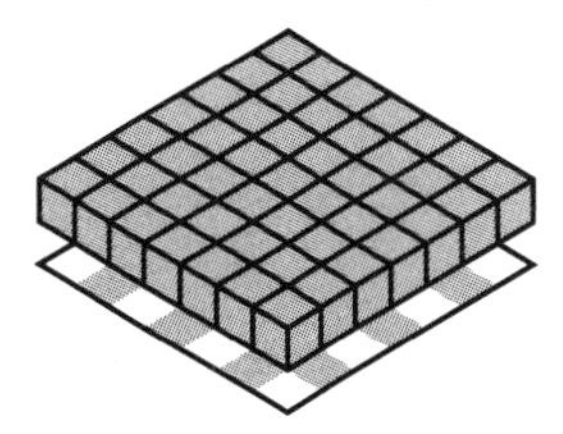

The height of the cube is 6 cm, which means that it takes 6 layers of these cubes to fill the prism. Forty-nine cubes in a layer times 6 layers is the number of cubes it takes to fill the prism. The volume of the prism is 49 times 6, which is equal to 294 cubic centimeters.

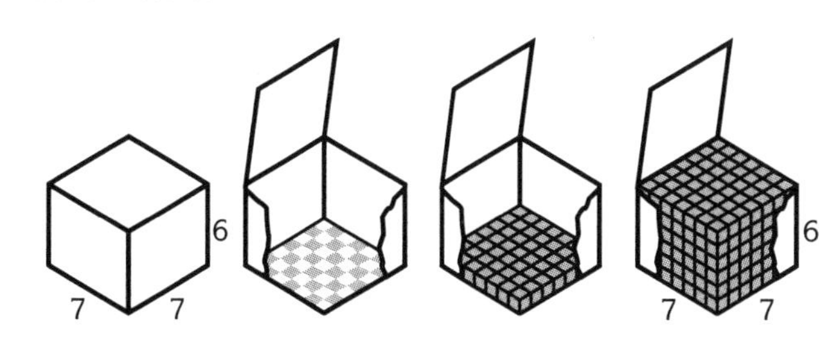

The **volume of a square-based prism** is the **area of the base** (which is the number of cubes in a layer) **times the height** (which is the number of layers of cubes needed to fill the prism).

Volume of a Triangular-Based Prism

In order to pack layers of cubes to fill a triangular prism, some of the cubes must be cut in half along a diagonal plane.

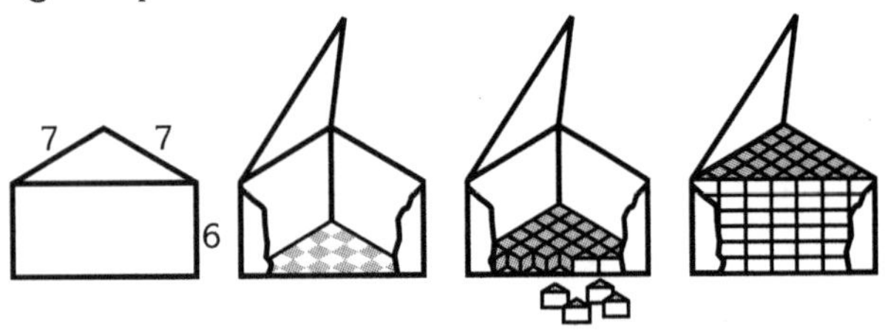

With the half cubes fitted into the base, it turns out that there are 24½ cubes in a layer. This is exactly the same as the area of the base, which is $\frac{1}{2} \cdot b \cdot h = \frac{1}{2} \cdot 7 \cdot 7$. Because the height is 6, it takes 6 layers to fill the prism. So, the **volume of the triangular prism is the area of the base times the height of the prism.**

Volume of a Cylinder

The area of the cylinder can be found in almost exactly the same way as we did the areas of the two prisms. A problem arises when fitting cubes into a layer of the cylinder; it requires quite a lot more than simply cutting a few of them in half as we did for the triangular prism. And even if the cubes could be cut in that way, how would students know how to accurately count them?

By now, from their experience with prisms, students should know that the number of cubes in a layer is the same as the area of the base. In this case, the diameter of the base is 7 and the radius is 3.5. The area is $\pi r^2 = 3.14 \cdot 3.5^2 = 38.5$ cm. The **volume of a cylinder is the area of the circular base times the height.**

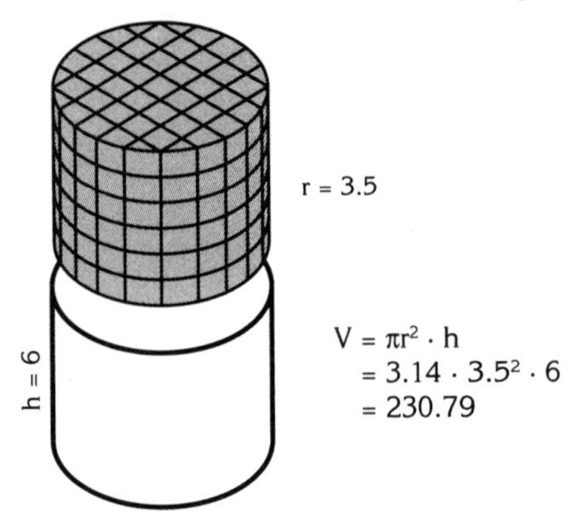

There is a very nice way to express the volume for each of these prisms and the cone with a single formula. **If B is the area of the base of a prism or cone and h is the height, then the formula for the volume is V = B·h.**

Measuring the Volume of Pyramids and Cones

While covering the base of a prism or cylinder requires cutting up some of the cubes, at least each layer of cubes needed to fill it is exactly the same. For a pyramid or cone, some of the cubes of the bottom layer will not only need to be cut, they will need to be cut at a slant, and each layer that gets stacked on top of another will need to be smaller and the cuts will be different. Hope for a formula!

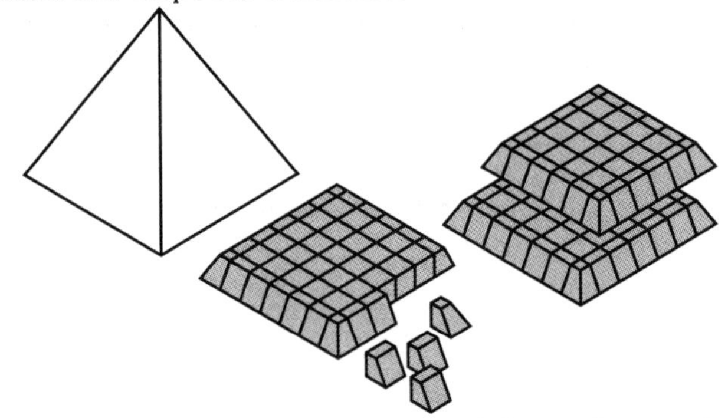

There is a formula for each of these shapes, but the only way to find it is by comparing the pyramid to a prism and the cone to a cylinder. In the activity, the square-based pyramid has the same base and height as the square-based prism; the triangular-based pyramid has the same base and height as the triangular-based prism; and the cone has the same circular base and height as the cylinder.

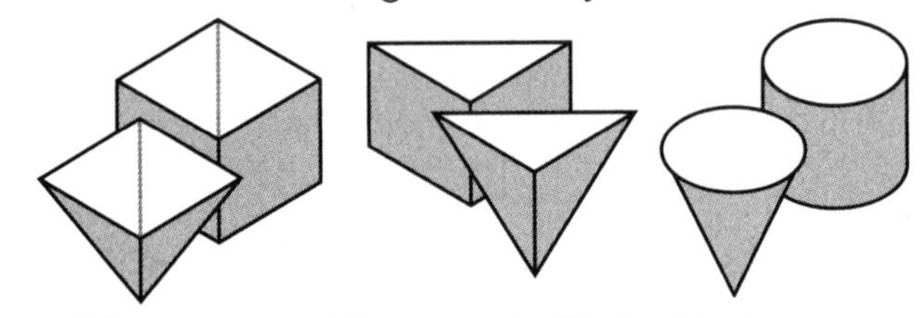

When a pyramid or cone is filled with rice or some similar material and then it is poured into the corresponding prism or cylinder, the result is that the prism or cylinder is filled to the one-third level. Alternatively, students will find that it takes three full pyramids or cones to fill the corresponding prism or cylinder. Consequently, the volume of a pyramid or cone is one-third the volume of a corresponding prism or cylinder (with the same base and height).

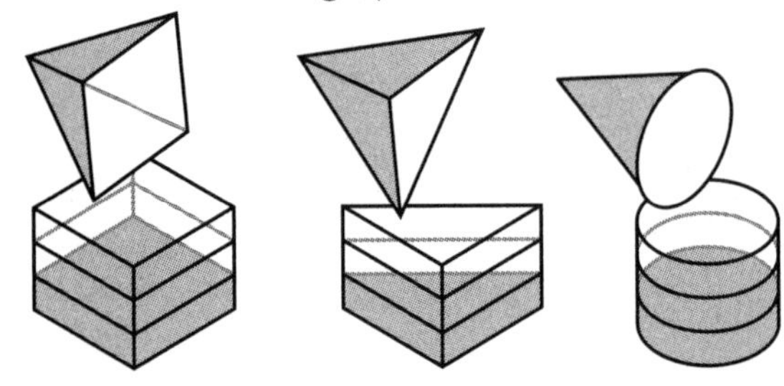

Just as there is a single formula for finding the volume of a prism or cylinder, there is a corresponding single formula for the volume of pyramids and cones. The formula is $V = 1/3 \cdot B \cdot h$, where B is the area of the base and h is the height.

Conclusion

Measuring three-dimensional shapes in this unit builds on what students know about measuring two-dimensional shapes. As students engage in the activities and they are helped to reflect back on what they did in this unit, they should recognize the extent to which they used what they already knew about measuring 2-D shapes to find the surface areas of 3-D shapes. Don't miss the opportunity to help students see and think about the parallels between finding areas of 2-D shapes and finding volumes of 3-D shapes. For example, the area of a rectangle or parallelogram can be thought of as the number of squares in a row (length or base) times the number of rows (height), while the volume of a prism or cylinder can be found by finding the number of cubes in a layer (area of base) and then multiplying by the number of layers (height). The formulas, $A = b \cdot h$ and $V = B \cdot h$, look very much alike. Similarly, there is a parallel between the way in which students were helped to make sense of the formula for the area of a triangle and the way in which students make sense of the formula for finding the volumes of pyramids and cones in this unit. To find the area of a triangle, we generally help students notice that two congruent triangles can be joined to form a parallelogram. Since the area of the parallelogram is $b \cdot h$, the area of one of the triangles must be $\frac{1}{2} \cdot b \cdot h$. In a similar way, by filling pyramids or cones and pouring their contents into a prism or cylinder having the same base and height, they discover the formula $V = \frac{1}{3} \cdot B \cdot h$ for the volume of a pyramid or cone. Again, the formulas, $A = \frac{1}{2} \cdot b \cdot h$ and $V = \frac{1}{3} \cdot B \cdot h$, look a lot alike.

Math and Science

The Model of Learning is a foundational component of AIMS lessons. It consists of four environments in which we learn about our world. These environments are represented by four geometric figures: a circle, a triangle, a square, and a hexagon.

An AIMS lesson will start with a *Key Question*. It is this question that leads students into an encounter with the four environments of learning.

For example, the Key Question for an activity might be: "How does the length of a piece of rope change if you tie knots in it?"

The circle corresponds to the real world. It involves *doing* something with or to concrete objects. This environment emphasizes the use of sensory input, involving *observing, touching (taking apart/putting together), smelling, hearing, tasting*. Observations here can be qualitative or quantitative (counting and measuring). The use of multiple senses causes activity in the parts of the brain where that type of information is processed, thus establishing or reinforcing mental connectors.

The activity would begin in the circle with students tying knots one by one in a piece of rope and measuring the length of the rope each time another knot is tied.

The triangle represents the abstractions of *reading* and *writing*. It is the real world symbolized in words and numbers. Meaning is attached to these abstractions because of what was done in the circle. This environment consists of recording numbers that result from the counting and measuring. It may involve writing a description of what was observed. Reading the rubber band books or comics found in the AIMS materials are included in this environment. Students work here when they read their textbooks or do the computation exercises.

In the knot-tying example, the students would next move to the triangle where the number of knots and the length of the rope are recorded in a table.

The square represents *picturing* or *illustrating* the real world. Graphs, diagrams, drawings, or an isometric drawing are examples of the pictures that can be used. The square might simply involve picturing what was recorded in the triangle. It could also be an illustration of an object or event that occurred while students were working in the circle environment. Both of these situations are constructed from student input; however, the drawing or graph or other illustration could be one that is imposed upon a student for interpretation purposes.

Relating to the example of tying knots, the student might move from the triangle to the square to construct a graph of the relationship between the number of knots in the rope and the length of the rope. Or the student could have moved directly from the circle to the square to construct the graph.

Finally, the hexagon represents *thinking, analyzing, generalizing, creating formulas, hypothesizing,* and *applying*. What did we find out? What does it mean? Is there a relationship? What is it? Is there a formula? To what other situations might this apply?

Students in the example might look back at the table and be asked, "By how much does the length of the rope change each time another knot is tied? How does this show up in the graph?" Students might note that the graph is a line. "What is the slope of the line? How does the slope show up in the table? What would be the length if there were 10 knots in the rope? How about if there were n knots in the rope? How could you find the length without measuring? Could you write this as an equation?"

The arrows pointing to and away from each of the environments suggest the importance of moving back and forth between the environments. To generalize the relationship between the number of knots and the length of the rope required going back and forth between the hexagon, the square, and the triangle. Once the formula is found, it can be applied to another situation that might be posed in the circle.

Perhaps the most important thing the Model of Learning does is to remind us of the four learning environments and help us think about how to structure an activity or lesson so that students are constructing and reinforcing the concepts and relationships. This is accomplished by moving back and forth between these environments. The triangle is where students too often spend most of their time in school activities. While this environment is not unimportant, the other environments give students something other than the tip of their pencil with which to think. AIMS activities are designed around these environments and make moving back and forth between these environments natural and meaningful.

Model of Learning